MW00632905

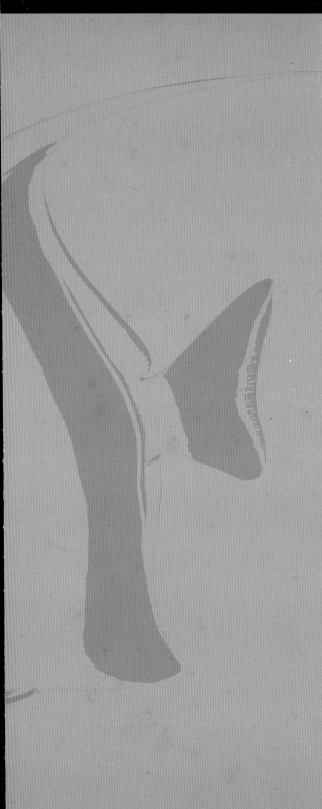

Kuiter, Rudie H., and Helmut Debelius: Surgeonfishes, Rabbitfishes and Their Relatives

First English language edition 2001

Published by TMC Publishing, Chorleywood, UK

Responsibility of text and taxonomic decisions: Rudie H. Kuiter and Helmut Debelius.

Print and production: Grupo M & G Difusión S.L.

TMC Publishing
Solesbridge Lane,
Chorleywood, Herts WD3 5SX
United Kingdom

Tel: +44 (0) 1923 284151   Fax: +44 (0) 1923 285840
Email: info@tmc-publishing.com
Website: www.tmc-publishing.com

ISBN 0-9539097-1-9

The Marine Fish Families Series

Surgeonfishes, Rabbitfishes
and their relatives

A Comprehensive Guide
to Acanthuroidei

Rudie H Kuiter . Helmut Debelius

TMC
publishing

TMC Publishing, Chorleywood, UK

ACKNOWLEDGEMENTS: We are most grateful to the contributors who supplied us with information and many photographs to make this work complete. Valuable data on diets and speciation were supplied by Kendall Clements (University of Auckland) and Howard Choat (James Cook University) who have studied the diet of acanthurid fishes for many years and have analysed various species-complexes with the use of DNA sequencing. Jerry Allen, Roger Steene and Neville Coleman also generously supplied many photographs.

Photo-credits: Contributing photographers are credited in the captions. All other photographs are by the authors.

TABLE OF CONTENTS

INTRODUCTION

The acanthuroids comprise several large and important tropical reef fish families which are mostly herbivorous. They include the fishes popularly known as surgeonfishes or tangs, unicorns, sawtails, the Moorish Idol, and rabbitfishes. Most groups and species are variously distributed in tropical to subtropical seas of the Indo-Pacific, but surgeonfishes and sawtails have representatives world-wide. Many members of these groups help to keep in check the fast growing algae that does especially well on sunny, shallow reefs. Their occurrence in great numbers keeps coral reefs from becoming overgrown and also makes certain that other vegetation, such as seagrasses, is regularly cleaned, especially by juvenile rabbitfishes, ensuring good light capture and healthy beds. Surgeonfishes even graze on other animals, such as turtles, that have problems with algae, further highlighting their important role in the reefs. Many of the small and colourful species are popular aquarium fish, whilst the larger ones are often featured in public aquariums. The rabbitfish is valued as a food fish and is locally important. Recently the batfishes, spadefishes, luvars (very deep water only - not included) and scats were classified as acanthuroid fishes which are planktivores, omnivores and scavengers and are here presented as relatives of the surgeonfish.

SELECTED ACANTHUROID FAMILY REPRESENTATIVES

SURGEONFISHES
ACANTHURINAE *18*

MOORISH IDOL
ZANCLIDAE *139*

RABBITFISHES
SIGANIDAE *142*

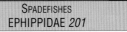

SPADEFISHES
EPHIPPIDAE *201*

UNICORNS
NASINAE *96*

SAWTAILS
PRIONURINAE *130*

BATFISHES
EPHIPPIDAE *180*

SCATS
SCATOPHAGIDAE *205*

Whilst the majority of fish species on tropical reefs are predators, the herbivores make up for it with their sheer numbers, with many of the species occurring in massive schools. The surgeonfishes are the best known herbivores, as they are common and the most colourful, and also have the widest distribution. The diver as well as the snorkeller above can admire these elegant, nimble swimmers as they graze openly in the relatively shallow habitats. This behaviour makes it easy for fish collectors, who can surround them with their nets, and is one of the reasons why surgeonfishes are readily available in shops.

ABOUT SURGEONFISHES, UNICORNFISHES AND SAWTAILS

The common name 'surgeonfish' is derived from a characteristic that clearly distinguishes Acanthuridae from other fish families: the spines or "scalpels" on the caudal peduncle, one or more on each side. Based primarily on differences in this characteristic, the family can be divided into three subfamilies. The Acanthurinae, in which the peduncular spine rests in a groove and can be erected in defence or during fights, and the Nasinae and Prionurinae in which the peduncular feature is arranged as one or more fixed blades on each side, that are sharp and elongate with age. The Nasinae members are commonly called 'unicorns' because of the single horn-like feature that develops on the male's forehead in several of the species, and Prionurinae 'sawtails' in relation to the series of fixed peduncular spines. The peduncular spines are often outlined and highlighted by bright colours (warning colouration). Although the peduncular spine in the Acanthurinae can be erected, there is no muscular function between the spine and the fish's body, and the spine is raised as the tail curves, and at a radius of about 80° it emerges fully on the outward curve of the tail. This event is readily observed when a mirror is placed in front of an aquarium that is the home of a territorial surgeonfish. As soon as it discovers the "intruder" it spreads all its fins, charges towards the mirror image, and whips its caudal peduncle at the perceived new arrival. These spines cause painful flesh wounds and it is wise to use caution when handling surgeonfishes. It is thought that in some species in Acanthurinae the spines are venomous, but detailed studies on many members have been unable to confirm this. On the other hand, experiments with members of Nasinae and Prionurinae have proven that the spines or their surrounding tissues are venomous. Fishes have died from injuries which were inflicted from spines of a prionurid surgeonfish.

The scalpel-like spine of Acanthurinae, *Acanthurus sohal*, slightly raised.

The fixed tail-spines of Nasinae, double and hooked forward in *Naso elegans*.

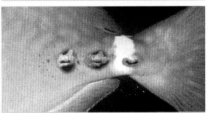

The saw-like series of tail-spines of the Prionurinae, *Prionurus maculatus*.

Sexual dimorphism. The male of *Naso brachycentron* has a distinctive horn, whilst the female has none. Differences between males and females are minor in most groups of surgeonfishes, unicornfishes or sawtails. In general, males grow larger than females, in all unicorn species males have bigger peduncular knives, some males grow a larger horn than females, or only males develop a hump on forehead or back. Such features are missing in the juvenile stages and it is almost impossible to tell which one will turn into a male or female. Photos are from the Maldives.

Sexual Dichromatism and Spawning

The nuptial colour of the normally drab dusky to brown, *Ctenochaetus striatus* has paled in colour for courtship and subsequent spawning. Sexual dichromatism exists primarily during the spawning season and often colours are for short durations, used only for display and courtship. The rest of the time the sexes are virtually identical in colour. Photo from the Maldives.

Spawning activities are generally tied to the lunar cycle and the biggest tides that provide strong currents to carry their produce far from the reef to start a pelagic larval stage. Some surgeonfishes spawn during a new moon, while others spawn around the time of the full moon, depending on the species or geography. Many surgeonfishes spawn together in a large group that masses late in the afternoon, coming together from various areas of the reef, whilst others may spawn strictly in pairs. The male seeks out the gravid female and demonstrates his readiness to spawn by changing colour and shimmying. Side by side the pair rise from the bottom, swimming towards the surface. At the apex of their ascent, both simultaneously release their gametes into the open water and when mass-spawning takes place, the gametes are so plentiful that they soon cloud the water. Males may mate with several females during such a session and sexually mature female surgeonfishes can spawn about once a month. The released eggs are targeted straight away by planktivores that have learned this routine and species range from small basslets or trevally to large mantas. When diving at sunset around reefs, divers have a chance to witness such an event.

Pelagic Stages

Acronurus is the stage towards the end of the pelagic life and prior to settling in the reef. The shape is now recognisable as an acanthurid. This 30 mm individual was photographed near the surface at night by diving in the lights of a large ship, about 1 km off the east coast of Sulawesi, Indonesia.

The tiny buoyant eggs, less than 1 mm in diameter, hatch within 2 days. The hatchlings are so rudimentary that the heart only begins to beat after some hours and this stage is referred to as **prolarval**. This pelagic stage has a round yolk-sac that is enormous, but absorbed in about two days, and it floats with its head down. As it develops it becomes less buoyant and has to make short-duration swims to remain near the surface. After four days, the more developed larval stage begins, feeding on plankton. At this stage it also begins to takes on more features, the body becomes compressed and large thorn-like spines develop in the dorsal and ventral fins. The thorns are probably poisonous and help protect the otherwise defenceless planktonic larvae. Towards the end of the pelagic stage and prior to settling in the reef, a stage is reached that is distinctive and called 'acronurus'. The body is now oval, the thorns in the fins disappear, blade-like spines develop on the caudal peduncle, and it is recognisable as a developing surgeonfish. These young are still transparent at a length of 25 mm or more. The complete planktonic stage may last about 10 weeks and some species can travel great distances in currents, a factor that contributes to the wide-ranging distribution of many of the species and a regular gene-flow between different populations. Afterwards, the young surgeonfishes settle in the shallow reef waters.

Post Larval and Juvenile Behaviour

The behaviour of young surgeonfishes varies considerably between different species and sometimes between different populations of the same species. This has much to do with competition for food and the threat from predators. Some juveniles are very territorial, but as adults they often form large schools that widely roam the reef. Surgeonfishes reach sexual maturity after about 2 years. Although some species have spawned in large public aquariums, reproduction in the home aquarium has not been reported.

The post-pelagic stage of a *Naso*, just settling on the substrate. This semi-transparent stage is called **prionurus**. Within days after settling, they change to the juvenile colour. Photo by Takamasa Tonozuka, Bali, Indonesia.

The juvenile stage of a *Naso unicornis*. Small juvenile unicorn-fishes appear solitary, but may mix with other acanthuroid juveniles. Some species occur in small aggregations and start schooling when sub-adult. NSW, Australia.

Mixed juveniles of *Acanthurus nigrofuscus* and *Prionurus microlepidotus*. Both species often occur in small groups of their own, but also mix with various other acanthurids of similar size during feeding. NSW, Australia.

Four juvenile species of *Acanthurus* swimming together. Left to right: *nigroris, olivaceus, triostegus* and below *nigrofuscus*. All are very young and prefer to stay close to the shelter of the rocks. NSW, Australia.

Juvenile *Zebrasoma veliferum* are typically seen alone amongst corals, but this small group of postlarval individuals was photographed sheltering amongst the arms of a crinoid. Photo: PNG, Bob Halstead.

Juvenile *Paracanthurus hepatus* typically school above *Acropora* thickets to feed on zooplankton. They stay close to the coral and at the first sign of danger dive into narrow crevices amongst the branches. Photo: Indonesia.

Distribution and Habitat of Acanthurinae, Nasinae and Prionurinae

Due to the long pelagic stages of young, many species are widespread, especially in the Acanthurinae and Nasinae, and this may also have contributed to speciation. The members of Prionurus have a much more localised distribution, but appear to have adapted to the cooler waters of subtropical seas. Some Acanthurid fossils from Europe, dating back more than 50 million years, are recognisable as the ancestors of present forms, such as the genus *Acanthurus, Naso* and the related *Zanclus*. Changes in shape or length of snout took place and various species evolved in different areas as conditions changed. Continental drift has much to do with the present distribution of species, especially between the Atlantic and Pacific Oceans.

Of the Acanthurinae, the most speciose genus, *Acanthurus,* has representatives in all tropical seas, the closely related *Ctenochaetus* has a number of species and subspecies variously distributed throughout the Indo-Pacific, whilst the monotypic *Paracanthurus* is only found in the Indo-West Pacific. There are various examples of closely related species, subspecies or geographical variations between various geographical zones, especially the Pacific and Indian Oceans, and some areas such as the Red Sea or remote locations have their own localised colour-morph or species. The differences between many of these forms or sibling species are small and indicate a recent speciation and the continuing process of speciation. In many cases there is no clear separation between forms and it may require molecular work to get a clearer picture on some of these species-complexes. The genus *Zebrasoma* has representatives throughout the Indo-Pacific, but the species are much more localised. The exception, *Z. scopas,* shows considerable geographical variation. As adults, most surgeonfishes live in relatively shallow water where they specialise in feeding on certain algaes that grow on hard surfaces such as rock, rubble or dead coral. Few species prefer to feed on zooplankton and in most cases they will feed on both when there is a need. Some species such as *Paracanthurus* appear to feed exclusively on zooplankton when young, but also graze algae as adults. Acanthurids are particularly numerous in the tropical oceanic regions where the water is nearly always very clear and exposed to direct sunlight. The algae grows rapidly and is continuously grazed by the surgeons, giving it little chance to smother the various invertebrates. A number of species, those in *Ctenochaetus* and some in *Acanthurus,* feed on detritus, taking in sand with it. These species have a gizzard-like stomach with thick walls to protect it. Most species occur in coastal waters, entering harbours and estuaries when young. There are less species in oceanic places, but greater numbers.

The Nasinae is represented by the single genus *Naso*. Representatives are found throughout the tropical Indo-Pacific and none in the Atlantic. There are a number of variations in form and maximum size, most are widespread and show little or no variation between different geographical zones. Juveniles occur singly or in small loose aggregations in shallow coastal waters or in reef-lagoons and feed on algae. Adults usually form schools and feed primarily on plankton, especially in reef-channels or along outer reef walls that are subject to strong currents and occur at various depths. Some have been reported at depths of over 100 m.

The Prionurinae is represented by the single genus *Prionurus*. Representatives are found in the tropical to subtropical seas of the Indo-Pacific and the Atlantic. All the species are localised and this appears to be caused by their preference to cooler water, and warm waters may act as a barrier to disperse further. The larval stage is similar to that of the other acanthurids and in many areas is taken by currents to cooler conditions, rather than to more tropical ones. The adults form large schools on coastal, as well as off-shore, rocky reefs and graze on algae from the bottom as well as feeding on plankton at the surface. Juveniles are usually seen in small groups, grazing algae from rocks in shallow coastal bays, estuaries, or lagoons.

Mixed surgeons feasting on the algal growth on a turtle, who is obviously enjoying it and is assisting by raising its head. Getting rid of algae greatly assists the turtle in keeping clean and in maintaining healthier skin. If left unchecked the algae becomes long and difficult to swim with. The shot was taken in Hawaii where, as in many other Pacific locations, the surgeons occur in great numbers. The rubble below is well grazed by them and the various species are giving the turtle a good work-over to satisfy their appetite. Photo: Doug Perrine.

Acanthurus coeruleus being cleaned by goby **A** and shrimp **B**. The individual with the goby has paled in colour which probably helps the goby to find parasites. The individual with the shrimp remains dark. The goby looks for the parasite visually, but the shrimp works by touch. Photos in Bonaire by Otto Gremblewski.

A

An *Acanthurus thompsoni* with scars from probable fights, visiting a cleaning station with several juvenile *Bodianus diana*. The same individual in the two photographs, changing colour from when it arrived **A** from its almost black body to a pale colouration in **B**. The paling may highlight the problems around the wounds or show up parasites to make it easier for the cleaner wrasses to find. Photos in the Maldives. **B**

The normally very dark-looking *Naso vlamingii* has paled considerably for the cleaner wrasse that is inspecting the dorsal fin. Schooling unicornfishes usually visit cleaning stations in the afternoon and may line up in large numbers, each waiting patiently to get a service. Photo in Bali, Indonesia.

A Question of Survival

This 40 mm juvenile *Prionurus microlepidotus* has lost its whole tail and part of its body to a Tailor *Pomatomus saltatrix* (called Bluefish in America and Elf in South Africa). Amazingly this little sawtail was found grazing algae on the bottom and it swam very well by mainly using its pectoral fins. Since all the digestive organs were left untouched by the bite, it survived, but it lost its defensive venomous spines and the ability to escape a further predator. How long will its luck last? Photo: Tuncurry, NSW, Australia.

Acanthurids in the Aquarium

These small and colourful species are popular with marine aquarists around the world and they can provide impressive displays of colour. The bright blue *Paracanthurus hepatus* or the delightful yellow *Zebrasoma flavescens* are particularly wonderful as they can be kept in small groups. Others may be territorial and may have to be kept as a single individual of that species with others to avoid nasty disputes. In large aquariums there are less problems with species, even territorial ones, as individuals may be happy with a section of the space available and the weaker individual can stay away from a dominant one. The larger species, such as the unicornfishes, are only suitable for very large aquariums as shown below.

The large reef tank in the Expo Aquarium in Okinawa, Japan, accommodates a great variety of fish, including *Naso* and *Acanthurus*.

Paracanthurus hepatus. Juveniles from the Philippines in a home aquarium, sharing with *Acanthurus japonicus* & *A. pyroferus.*

Paracanthurus hepatus. The Indian Ocean form kept in the Monaco public aquarium.

From the moment the fishes are collected, appropriate care is essential to provide healthy specimens to the customer. Apart from having good water conditions, the right temperature, etc, it is important to know the behaviour of the various species. Which fish can travel together and those that need to be kept apart.

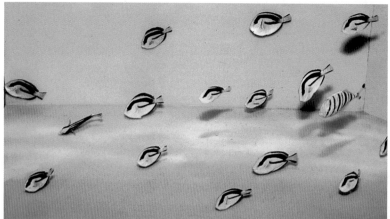

Arriving at the importer: here too, the facilities have to accommodate special requirements. Fighting fish can do a lot of damage to each other and that can result in diseases from infected wounds or even death. Established dealers keep the fish in quarantine for some time to make sure that fish are disease free before they go into the shops.

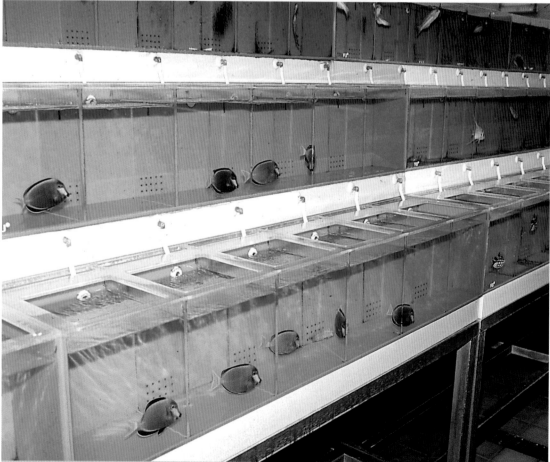

The holding facilities of TMC in England. Territorial species are individually held, whilst those that get along are kept together.

Purchasing Acanthurids

There is a wide range of species available but it is important to determine the suitability of the potential new pet before purchasing. Especially when it concerns a small home aquarium where space is limited and only small species are likely to be happy. It may be very tempting to buy a beautiful small juvenile fish, but it may outgrow its new home in no time at all. All the species of surgeonfish grow fast, especially when young, and it is best to avoid the larger species if space is likely to become an issue.

The most important thing is to look for healthy specimens. The fins should be intact and show no sign of discolouration, such as whitish blotches or spots, in the clear parts. The sides of undernourished specimens show signs of "caving-in", usually along the back just below the dorsal fin and these individuals may have refused food or were starved. In most cases such fish have little chance of recovering in community tanks and need special care. Such fish are weak and may also have no resistance to any disease they come into contact with.

Unless you have a very large home aquarium, you should stick to members of the Acanthurinae only, leaving unicornfishes or sawtails to public aquariums.

Taking Care of Acanthurids

All surgeonfishes are busy swimmers and need space. The bigger the aquarium the better. They like swimming in and around things, as well as in large open spaces, and good rock formations are essential for happy fish. They normally sleep in crevices and some also like to retreat to these for a rest at times during the day. In the wild, surgeons live in shallow waters, usually high energy zones, which are rich in oxygen and of a high quality. Maintaining good water quality is very important in the aquarium and this usually becomes difficult and degrades when many fish are kept, leading to bacteria build-up to which surgeonfishes are sensitive. There are various ways of ensuring water quality and combatting bacteria, such as with UV lights and biological control. However, serious marine aquarists now have elaborate systems and good knowledge to maintain the highest standards. For those who lack the ability at this stage it is necessary to consult an expert.

Introducing a new surgeonfish into an aquarium is usually a problem when it already houses other surgeonfishes. The established individuals reject most newcomers and releasing it into the tank will probably result in chasing, fighting or the newcomer hiding in a hole, too scared to come out. In small aquariums it is a major problem and if it involves only one other fish, it may be best to take the established fish out for a few days and let the new one settle in before returning the old one. Partitioning a section of the aquarium for a few days with a piece of glass may work in some cases. When there are no surgeonfishes in the aquarium, one can introduce several species together and they will probably accept each other without problems. Always keep an eye on the situation for a few days and make sure that the newcomer gets some food to eat.

Feeding the correct food is most important with these fishes. They are herbivores by nature and they need a plant-based diet to stay healthy. Most species that are sold feed on algae mixed with some plankton in their natural environment. Most prefer the fine hair-like algae that grows on rubble and the surface of seagrasses and the diet may change during different stages in life. With good lights, the aquarium will produce some algae but unless it is enormous, probably not enough for these fishes that normally consume a large quantity. Those species for which the diet is mainly algae will have problems with internal infection and blockages if fed only meat-based products Check with your local supplier about the availability of a vegetable-based food. The use of commercial vegetables is possible, but it is best to grow your own in compost, as in many countries such products contain high amounts of insecticides.

Table 1. Fin-formulas of Species of Acanthurinae.

	Dorsal fin		Anal fin		Pectoral fin	Ventral fin
Paracanthurus hepatus	IX	19–20	III	18–19	16	I, 3
Acanthurus achilles	IX	29–33	III	26–29	16	I, 5
Acanthurus albipectoralis	IX	25	III	23	16–17	I, 5
Acanthurus auranticavus	IX	25–26	III	23–24	16–17	I, 5
Acanthurus bahianus	IX	23–26	III	21–23	15–17	I, 5
Acanthurus bariene	IX	26–28	III	25–26	17	I, 5
Acanthurus blochi	IX	25–27	III	23–25	17	I, 5
Acanthurus chirurgus	IX	24–25	III	22–23	16–17	I, 5
Acanthurus coeruleus	IX	26–28	III	24–26	16–17	I, 5
Acanthurus dussumieri	IX	25–27	III	24–26	16–17	I, 5
Acanthurus fowleri	IX	26–27	III	25–26	16–17	I, 5
Acanthurus gahhm	IX	25–26	III	23–25	16–17	I, 5
Acanthurus grammoptilus	IX	25–26	III	23–24	16–17	I, 5
Acanthurus guttatus	IX	27–30	III	23–26	15–17	I, 5
Acanthurus japonicus	IX	28	III	26	16	I, 5
Acanthurus leucocheilus	IX	24–25	III	23	16–17	I, 5
Acanthurus leucopareius	IX	25–27	III	23–25	16–17	I, 5
Acanthurus leucosternon	IX	28–30	III	23–26	15–16	I, 5
Acanthurus lineatus	IX	27–30	III	25–28	16–17	I, 5
Acanthurus maculiceps	IX	24–26	III	22–24	16–17	I, 5
Acanthurus mata	IX	24–26	III	23–24	16–17	I, 5
Acanthurus monroviae	IX		III			I, 5
Acanthurus nigricans	IX	28–32	III	26–29	16	I, 5
Acanthurus nigricaudus	IX	24–28	III	23–26	16–17	I, 5
Acanthurus nigrofuscus	IX	24–27	III	22–24	16–17	I, 5
Acanthurus nigroris	IX	24–27	III	23–25	15–16	I, 5
Acanthurus nubilus	IX	25–27	III	23–24	16–17	I, 5
Acanthurus olivaceus	IX	23–25	III	22–24	15–17	I, 5
Acanthurus polyzona	IX	22–24	III	21–23	16	I, 5
Acanthurus sohal	IX	30–31	III	28–29	17	I, 5
Acanthurus tennentii	IX	23–24	III	22–23	16	I, 5
Acanthurus thompsoni	IX	23–26	III	23–26	16–19	I, 5
Acanthurus triostegus	IX	22–24	III	19–22	14–16	I, 5
Acanthurus xanthopterus	IX	25–27	III	23–25	16–17	I, 5
Acanthurus pyroferus	VIII	27–30	III	24–28	16	I, 5
Acanthurus tristis	VIII	27–30	III	24–28	16	I, 5
Ctenochaetus binotatus	VIII	24–27	III	22–25	15–16	I, 5
Ctenochaetus flavicauda	VIII	25–27	III	22–25	15–16	I, 5
Ctenochaetus hawaiensis	VIII	27–29	III	25–26	16	I, 5
Ctenochaetus marginatus	VIII	27–28	III	25	16–17	I, 5
Ctenochaetus striatus	VIII	27–31	III	24–28	16–17	I, 5
Ctenochaetus strigosus	VIII	25–27	III	22–25	15–16	I, 5
Ctenochaetus cf *strigosus*	VIII	25–27	III	22–25	15–16	I, 5
Ctenochaetus sp	VIII	25–27	III	22–25	15–16	I, 5
Ctenochaetus tominiensis	VIII	24–25	III	22–23	15–16	I, 5
Zebrasoma desjardinii	IV	27–31	III	22–24	15–17	I, 5
Zebrasoma flavescens	V	23–26	III	19–22	14–16	I, 5
Zebrasoma gemmatum	IV	27–28	III	24–25	16–17	I, 5
Zebrasoma rostratum	V	24–25	III	19–20	14–16	I, 5
Zebrasoma scopas	V	23–26	III	19–21	14–16	I, 5
Zebrasoma veliferum	IV	28–32	III	22–26	15–17	I, 5
Zebrasoma xanthurum	V	24–25	III	19–20	15	I, 5

Fig. 1. Selected Features of Acanthurinae genera.

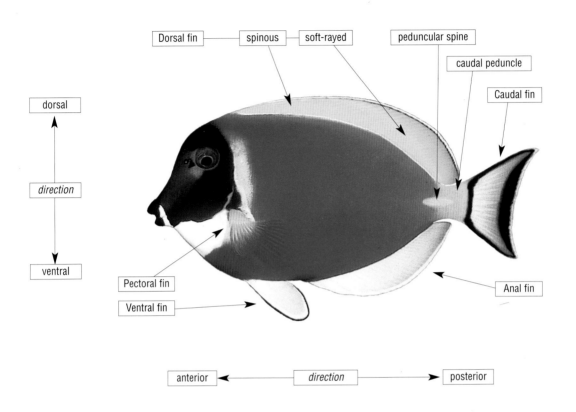

KEY TO ACANTHURINAE GENERA

1a	Dorsal spines 4 or 5; dorsal and anal fins elevated	*Zebrasoma* (P. 83)
1b	Dorsal spines 9; dorsal and anal fins not elevated	.2
1c	Dorsal spines 8; dorsal and anal fins not elevated	.3

2a	Ventral fin with 1 spine and 3 rays	*Paracanthurus* (P. 69)
2b	Ventral fin with 1 spine and 5 rays	*Acanthurus* (P. 34)

3a	Teeth on jaws fixed, thin, incurved, edges denticulate: upper teeth fewer than 26	
	....	*Acanthurus* (P. 26)
3b	Teeth movable, attenuate with incurved and denticulate tips: upper teeth more than 30	
	....	*Ctenochaetus* (P. 72)

Note: This key is intended to be used with preserved material or small individuals that may lack colour. Large individuals and living fishes are readily identified by their colouration and general shape.

FAMILY **ACANTHURIDAE – SURGEONFISHES, UNICORNFISHES AND SAWTAILS**

A large family of tropical to subtropical reef-fishes, playing an important role in the ecosystem. Comprises 3 subfamilies - the Acanthurinae, the surgeonfishes, characterised in part by a sharp peduncular spine that folds into a groove; Nasinae, the unicornfishes, with one or two bony plates on the peduncle, which bear sharp keels or fixed spines in adults; and Prionurinae, the sawtails, with a series of bony plates on the peduncle that bear venomous spines. Most species are primarily herbivorous, feeding largely on algae and are usually present in large numbers on coral reefs, preventing them from becoming dominant. Few feed on plankton as juveniles or when adult, depending on the species.

ACANTHURINAE 18–95

NASINAE 96–129

PRIONURINAE 130–138

SUBFAMILY **ACANTHURINAE – SURGEONFISHES**

The subfamily Acanthurinae is the largest of the acanthuroid groups with 4 genera and about 55 species. Surgeonfishes are oblong to ovate shaped and have a highly compressed body that is covered with tiny ctenoid scales. They have a single long-based low and even dorsal fin that originates above the head, the caudal fin is normally truncate to very lunate (rounded in some juveniles), and the pectoral fins are large and pointed. The mouth is small, but conspicious and placed low, well below the body axis, with numerous small teeth in jaws that differ in characteristics between genera. Eyes are placed high but laterally on the head. The peduncular spine is slender and sharp, folds into a groove, and is thought to be venomous in some species.

Most species graze on algae or take detritus from various surfaces, including rock, coral and seagrass, that are scraped with their rows of fine teeth, which in some species are movable enabling them to enter narrow ridges. Nearly all species are primarily herbivorous, but many feed occasionally amongst zooplankton during tidal currents to supplement their diet and a few switch over to or from zooplankton as their main diet at a later stage in life. Adults of the larger species are usually seen grazing on the substrate in small groups, whilst the smaller ones may form large schools, especially in areas where habitats are defended by damselfishes. Being in large numbers enables them to completely overwhelm the damselfishes that can only chase a few individuals. Some species congregate in large numbers to spawn, choosing particular areas that produce strong currents to carry their gametes far away from the reefs. They produce numerous tiny eggs, less than 1 mm in diameter, and pelagic larval stages grow to about 30–40 mm long when returning to reefs to settle on the substrate. The post larval juveniles quickly become pigmented and live secreted on shallow substrates amongst rocks or rubble. They soon form small groups, often comprising various species, and such aggregations may include similar sized fishes from other families such as Chaetodontidae or Balistidae, to give them more freedom to graze near their hide-outs.

| Acanthurus 26 | Acanthurus 34 | Acanthurus 41 |
| Paracanthurus 69 | Ctenochaetus 72 | Zebrasoma 83 |

GENUS *Acanthurus* Forsskål, 1775 (as a subgenus of *Chaetodon*)

Masculine. Type species: *Chaetodon sohal* Forsskål, 1775. There are 36 known species of *Acanthurus* and it seems unlikely that many more will be discovered. Some, presently regarded as geographical variations, may prove to be different species when studied in more detail or by alternative techniques, such as molecular DNA sequencing. Recognising closely related species will remain an issue for many taxonomists who are not intimately associated with the group. What are clearly different species to one author may be problematic to another. Often it is the case that one can see differences while the other is blinded by similarities. However, species are based on differences, and similarities may indicate close relationships. Due to the dispersal of larval fishes, the members in *Acanthurus* are generally widespread, some throughout the Indo-Pacific, but a few are more localised in areas where populations may have been isolated for a long time, such as in the Red Sea. Differences between Indian and Pacific Oceans are generally minor compared to many other reef fish families. Although all the species are diagnostic in colour, they can be highly variable, changing colour with mood, day or night, and may change drastically with growth.

Characteristics of the genus *Acanthurus*.
Oval body, depth about 1.5–2.5 times in SL; caudal peduncle compressed, depth about 2–3 times in head length; dorsal-fin spines usually IX (VIII in 2 out of 36 species); anal-fin spines III; ventral fin I, 5; teeth on jaws fixed, incurved, thin and wide with denticulate edges; upper teeth fewer than 26; scales with ctenii on posterior margins.

The transparent larval stages are pelagic, oceanic and are completely solitary. When settling on the substrate they hide at first in crevices amongst rubble or rocks, but to feed on algae they need to come out in the open. The tiny surgeons are extremely wary, quickly retreating when approached, but team up at the first opportunity with other, similarly sized fishes that feed on the bottom. Small groups of mixed species are often seen roaming the shallow reef edges, and such groups could include a variety of other fishes, all seeking protection in numbers. The chances of teaming up with their own species increases over time and larger juveniles that school usually comprise of a single species. However, when it comes to feeding, the mixed species behaviour remains in many areas even when adult.

Adult schooling behaviour differs between species, and it may differ within a species between different geographical locations. Fishes in continental waters may behave dramatically different from those in oceanic zones, due to competition, predation pressure or other species of the same genus co-occurring. In addition, in some areas damselfishes are very territorial and protect their small patch of reef vigorously from intruders. When there are many such damselfishes, it may be difficult for surgeonfishes to get close to its food source - the algae that is growing where the damselfishes live. Here too, surgeonfishes school in great numbers, descending to the bottom and completely overwhelming the damselfish which has no chance to chase more than a few. In the Indo-Malay region with its high diversity, few species form large schools, but some of the same species form massive schools in some parts of the central Pacific where diversity is low. Circumstances too can change such behaviour. The aftermath of earthquakes, hurricanes, or coral bleaching, may give rise to an outbreak of algae growth due to the loss of corals or the many new, clean surfaces to grow on. This changed habitat may be less suited to many fishes but is ideal for surgeons (and parrot fishes) and the quick-growing juveniles take care of this 'problem' the following season as they roam the reef in schools, cleaning up the algae. In turn, space is created for corals to settle and on the tropical reefs in Indonesia, recovery of coral gardens is usually within 10 years (merely a blink of the eye in evolutionary terms) and generally looks even better then before.

Whilst some species occur in schools as a regular habit, some only congregate in large numbers to spawn in the particular places and at the particular times that favour the best chances for their offspring. Such places are usually on corners of reef channels, where large tides sweep past, taking the gametes a long way from the reef to open waters, and where predators are less numerous. By spawning in large numbers, so many eggs are produced that it soon fills up the local hungry fish, and the majority drift out to begin their

Small juveniles of *Acanthurus* usually form small groups amongst rocky boulders that provide algae on the sides or upper surfaces and shelter in the crevices. Occurring in numbers provides some safety in the more open areas where the food is. Shown here are mixed juveniles, about 40–45 mm long. Seal Rocks, New South Wales, inshore, 3 m deep. The barred *A. triostegus* and yellow *A. olivaceus* are easily identified, but dark species are more difficult and need closer examination. These ones are *A. nigroris*.

larval stage. In addition, such behaviour is just before dark when many fishes retreat to their resting places for the night, and this contributes to less eggs being eaten. Spawning sites may be well away from feeding areas, and species such as *Acanthurus triostegus* migrate regularly to such sites. Some of the larger species spawn in pairs, in small groups, or in some cases the same species may enjoy different strategies when occurring in low numbers. In most cases, males turn on a distinctive spawning colour (nuptial) as it approaches a female. If the female accepts, both rise slowly upwards and suddenly release their gametes high above the substrate together and quickly dash back to the bottom. Often the release is near the surface. A dramatic mass spawning of *Acanthurus guttatus* was observed by Helmut Debelius in the Cook Islands, which is documented over the following 2 pages.

Mixed species of *Acanthurus* adults. Maldives. The powder blue surgeon *Acanthurus leucosternon* is easily identified, but the dark species are more difficult, probably *A. nigricaudus*. Mixed species commonly roam to upper reefs in search for algae growth. They may graze an area clean of algae and revisit when sufficient regrowth appears. It keeps algae from becoming dominant in the shallows and this benefits the various corals.

Massing of adult *Acanthurus triostegus*. Cocos Keeling I., Indian Ocean. A lone powder blue surgeon *Acanthurus leucosternon* is in the foreground. Such large schools are usually either moving towards their spawning grounds or other areas to feed.

Acanthurus guttatus, massing on the bottom and changing colour to get ready for spawning. Cook Islands, South Pacific.

Acanthurus guttatus, spawning with several individuals near the surface, releasing gametes. Cook Islands. Peter Kragh.

Acanthurus guttatus (species account page 40), spawning. Clouds of gametes can be seen near the surface. Peter Kragh.

Spawning *Acanthurus guttatus*

It was after a late afternoon dive in the South Pacific Cook Islands. With a strong current running into the lagoon, I decided to snorkel to the outer edge of the channel for a while and let the current carry me back to the ship. I entered the water and could hardly believe my eyes: rows and rows of White-spotted Surgeonfish *Acanthurus guttatus* swimming to the Penrhyn Pass, coming from all directions. Not tens, not hundreds, but thousands of them in a seemingly endless stream. As I observed them in the slanting rays of the sun, I soon realised what was going on. Numerous small groups suddenly began shooting to the surface, each releasing a milky substance. Obviously a mass-spawning session! As I tried to get closer, the current was 'flying' me back into the lagoon and I cursed the fact that I hadn't bothered taking a camera.

Back on board I spread the news, and the following evening we were hoping for a repeat. With a new moon - peak spawning time for many fishes - we were camera-ready. The question was, how would we manage to stay put with a camera in a 5–6 knot current? One diver brought a steel cable to anchor himself to the reef. The rest of us were hanging on in small depressions or crevices along the shallow edge of the channel. An incredible sight, with more than ten thousand white-spotted surgeonfishes making their appearance and by now I could recognise the transformation colours of the spawning individuals. With so many fish it was impossible to make out the reef and the spawning spectacle soon began. When the groups of fishes shot up to the surface, egg and sperm were released simultaneously and each time it sounded almost like a shot under water. I didn't know where to look first, my legs were straining in the current and around me some divers were torn away from the reef. The fish totally ignored us and spawning was all around. It began to look like a London fog and it was difficult to focus the camera, but the film was already full. Someone took a photo of me and sent it to me. My eyes were bulging and my mouth was partly open, a true attestation of my fascination.

Helmut Debelius

Indo-Pacific *Acanthurus* Picture Index

leucosternon 26

cf *leucosternon* 27

nigricans 28

japonicus 29

achilles 30

nigroris 32

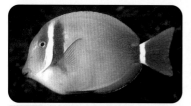
leucopareius 32

tristis 34

tristis 34

pyroferus 36

pyroferus 36

triostegus 38

polyzona 39

guttatus 40

grammoptilus 40

albipectoralis 41

thompsoni 42

nubilis 43

Indo-Pacific *Acanthurus* Picture Index

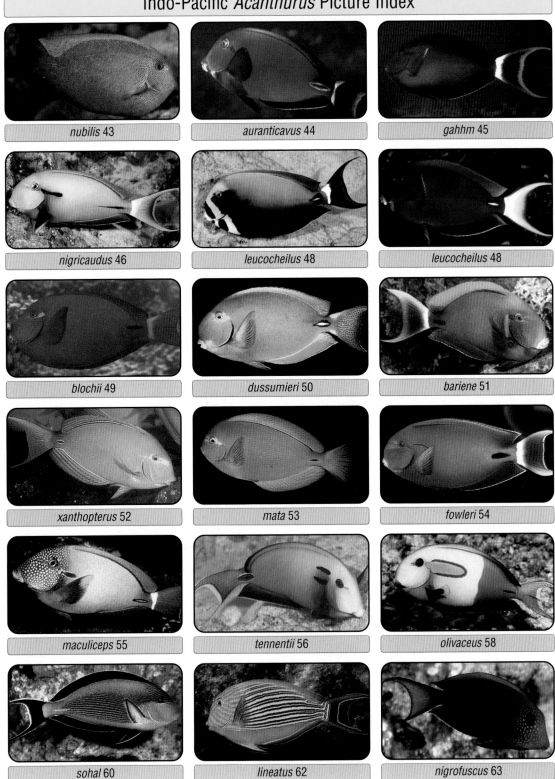

nubilis 43

auranticavus 44

gahhm 45

nigricaudus 46

leucocheilus 48

leucocheilus 48

blochii 49

dussumieri 50

bariene 51

xanthopterus 52

mata 53

fowleri 54

maculiceps 55

tennentii 56

olivaceus 58

sohal 60

lineatus 62

nigrofuscus 63

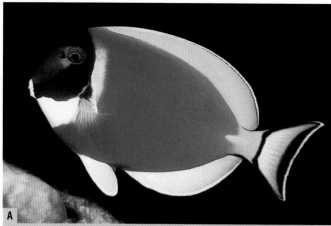

Indian Powderblue Surgeonfish
Acanthurus leucosternon

Acanthurus leucosternon Bennett, 1833. Sri Lanka.

Widespread Indian Ocean, ranging east to Christmas and Cocos Keeling Islands, and probably Sumatra, but replaced by similar species in Indonesia. Adults usually swim in small to large groups but may congregate in great numbers at times. Usually on shallow reef crests to about 20 m depth. Readily identified by the distinctive colouration that is similar from juvenile to adult stages, and distinguishable from similar Indonesian species by the white chest, yellow peduncle and black bands in the caudal fin. Length to 20 cm.

A. leucosternon. Maldives. Depth 7 m. Length 18 cm.

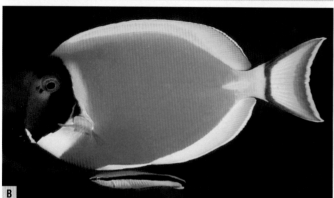

A. leucosternon. Seychelles. Depth 10 m. Length 20 cm. Neville Coleman.

A. leucosternon. Maldives. D. 7 m. L. 9 cm.

A. leucosternon. Maldives. Depth 10 m. Length 18 cm.

Indonesian Powderblue Surgeonfish
Acanthurus cf *leucosternon*
Undescribed species.

Southern Indonesia, ranging from Sumatra to west Flores and rare in Cocos and Christmas Is., eastern Indian Ocean, where the Indian Powderblue Surgeonfish is common. Found mainly around rocky reefs subject to strong currents and occurs alone or in small groups. *Acanthurus* cf *leucosternon* is best distinguished from *Acanthurus leucosternon* by the blue instead of white chest, dusky anal fin, and the yellow peduncular spine is not surrounded by yellow. Adults have a white horizontal blotch under the eye, similar to *A. nigricans,* and some ichthyologists presumed this species to be a hybrid between *A. leucosternon* and *A. nigricans.* Length to 20 cm.

A

A. cf *leucosternon.* Christmas I, I.O. Depth 10 m. Length 16 cm.

B

A. cf *leucosternon.* Komodo, Indonesia. Depth 25 m. Length 10 cm. Takamasa Tonozuka.

C

D

A. cf *leucosternon.* Java, Indonesia. Depth 15 m. Length 5 cm.

E

A. cf *leucosternon.* Southern Sunda Strait, Indonesia. Depth 7 m. Length 18 cm.

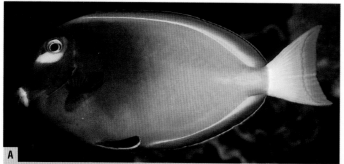

A. nigricans. Cook I, South Pacific. Depth 7 m. Length 14 cm.

Velvet Surgeonfish *Acanthurus nigricans*

Chaetodon nigricans. Linnaeus, 1758. No locality.
Acanthurus glaucopareius. Cuvier, 1831.

Widespread Indo-Pacific, showing no obvious differences throughout its large geographical range. Occurs mainly on outer reef crests in small to large aggregations when adult. Small juveniles are somewhat shy amongst large corals. Best distinguished from the similar *Acanthurus japonicus* by the relatively small white mark below the eye and sub-marginal yellow band in caudal fin. Length to 14 cm.

A. nigricans. Iriomote I., Japan. Depth 12 m. Length 12 cm.

A. nigricans. Sulawesi, Indonesia. Depth 5 m. Length 6 cm.

A. nigricans. Solomon I. D. 6 m. L. 14 cm. Neville Coleman.

A. nigricans. Tuvalu, South Pacific. D. 22 m. L. 12 cm.

A. nigricans. Christmas I, Indian Ocean. Depth 16 m. Length 14 cm.

White-nose Surgeonfish *Acanthurus japonicus*

Hepatus aliala japonicus. Schmidt, 1931. Japan.

Northern West Pacific, southern Japan, Philippines and Bonin I, Indonesia. Occurs on outer reef crests and slopes to about 20 m depth. Usually occurs in small to large aggregations. Very similar to *Acanthurus nigricans* in behaviour and looks. *A. japonicus* is best distinguished from *A. nigricans* by the large white area below the eye and the lack of the yellow sub-marginal band in the caudal fin. The two species co-occur in southern Japan and Bonin Islands. Length to 14 cm.

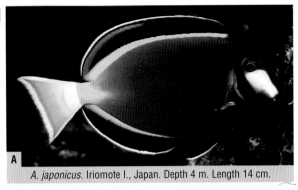

A. japonicus. Iriomote I., Japan. Depth 4 m. Length 14 cm.

A. japonicus. Philippines. Depth 3 m. Length 12 cm.

A. japonicus. Aquarium specimen from Philippines. Length 12 cm.

A. japonicus. Iriomote I., Japan. Depth 4 m. Length 14 cm.

Acanthurus achilles. Shaw, 1803. No locality.

Various Pacific Ocean localities, including Micronesia to Hawaiian Islands, New Caledonia and as far as the Marquesas, but is especially abundant in Polynesia Island region. Occurs primarily on exposed shallow reef flats. Adults are readily recognised by the large bright orange patch on the rear of the body, covering the peduncular spine. *Acanthurus achilles* hybridises with *A. nigricans* and this form was named *A. rackliffei*, Schultz, 1943. Length to 23 cm.

A. achilles. Hawaiian Islands. Depth 3 m. Length 22 cm.

A. achilles. Nancy Aquarium, France. Length 21 cm.

A. achilles. Aquarium, Japan. Length 22 cm.

D   *A. achilles*. Cook Islands, South Pacific. Depth 6 m. Length about 23 cm.

E   *A. achilles*. French Polynesia, South Pacific. Depth 6 m. Length about 23 cm. Peter Kragh.

Grey-head Surgeonfish *Acanthurus nigroris*

Acanthurus nigroris. Valenciennes, 1835. Hawaiian Is.

Widespread in the Pacific but mainly occurs in oceanic locations from Hawaiian Islands to the Coral Sea. Occurs on shallow exposed rocky reef, seen singly or in small loose groups. Adults identified by the pattern of fine bluish lines and the small black spots opposite each other at the ends of the bases of the dorsal and anal fins, head usually paled to a grey. Juveniles dusky, with faint lines but small and distinctive blue spots around eye and gill-cover margin. Length to 24 cm.

Note: known as Bluelined Surgeonfish in Hawaii, but this name is used in Japan, Philippines, Sri Lanka and other places for *Acanthurus lineatus.*

A

A. nigroris. Seal Rocks, NSW. Depth 3 m. Juvenile, length 50 mm.

B

A. nigroris. Hawaii. Adult. Length 22 cm. Kendall Clements.

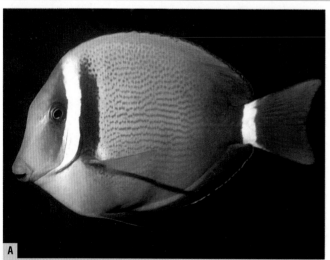

A

A. leucopareius. Hawaii. Kendall Clements.

White-bar Surgeonfish
Acanthurus leucopareius

Teuthis leucopareius. Jenkins, 1903. Hawaiian Islands.

Widespread in the Pacific in oceanic locations from Japan to Hawaiian Islands, and from New Caledonia Easter Island. Occurs on shallow exposed rocky reef and boulder habitat, forming schools where it is common, but ventures into deep water. Identified by the white bar on the head that is clearly visible from a distance. Length to 24 cm.

B   *A. leucopareius* with *A. triostegus*. Hawaii. Ed Robinson.

C   *A. leucopareius* with *A. nigroris* and *A. triostegus*. Hawaii. Ed Robinson.

Acanthurus tristis. Tickell, 1888. India.

Indian Ocean from Maldives and India to Bali. In Bali it co-occurs with *Acanthurus pyroferus,* the Pacific mimic surgeonfish. Coastal reef slopes and crests to about 20 m depth. Juveniles mimic *Centropyge eibli* and no other models are known for *A. tristis,* but may exist. Adults identified by white margin on caudal fin and black eye, usually surrounded by a lighter colour. Length to 20 cm.

See next page on mimicry.

A
A. tristis. Bali, Indonesia. Depth 15 m. Length 20 cm.

B
A. tristis. Sunda Strait, Indonesia. D. 20 m. L. 20 cm.

C
A. tristis. Maldives. Depth 10 m. Length 18 cm.

D
A. tristis. Andaman Sea. Depth 15 m. Length 20 cm.

E
A. tristis. Aquarium. Origin unknown. Length 75 mm.

F MIMIC
A. tristis. Bali, Indonesia. Depth 6 m. Length 50 mm.

G MODEL
Centropyge eibli. Bali, Indonesia. Depth 6 m. Length 50 mm.

The mimic surgeon *Acanthurus tristis* juvenile in the foreground, and its model pygmy angelfish *Centropyge eibli*, in the background. It takes an expert eye to tell them apart. Photo: Bali, Indonesia. Depth 5 m. Length about 8 cm.

Mimicry

The juveniles of two species of surgeonfishes, *Acanthurus tristis* and *A. pyroferus*, mimic pygmy angelfishes, *Centropyge* spp. In the Indian Ocean *Acanthurus tristis* mimics its model *Centropyge eibli* and in different areas of the West Pacific *Acanthurus pyroferus* mimics several different *Centropyge* species. Most common model is *C. vrolikii*, the Pacific sibling of *C. eibli*, but other models are *C. heraldi*, *C. flavissimus*, *C. bicolor*, and possibly others.

It is obvious that somehow the surgeonfish benefits by looking like the angelfish and our hypothesis is based on our own observations. Both belong to families that have pelagic larval stages, but they differ greatly in post larval sizes. Post larval *Centropyge* species measure only about 10–12 mm in total length, whilst post laval *Acanthurus* species measure about 30-40 mm in total length, depending on the species and when reaching reefs. Post larval *Centropyge* live secretively amongst rubble or in narrow crevices, feed on a variety of small invertebrates and gradually expand their territory, becoming more confident, with age and increasing size, about moving about. When the pygmy angel juveniles reach the size of a settling acanthurid, about 30–40 mm, they are totally familiar with their habitat and quite cunning. Aquarists, trying to catch them at that stage know all too well how difficult to capture these fishes are, and no doubt the local reef predator (such as a rock-cod or scorpionfish) has learned this too. Either the angelfish avoids predators with ease, or at that stage the angelfish is accepted by them as part of the local community, and is thus not considered prey. In contrast, acanthurid post larval juveniles settle at a much larger size, find it more difficult to hide easily, and need to come out in the open and more exposed parts on the shallow reef flats to satisfy their herbivorous appetite.

By looking like the 'cunning' and experienced pygmy angelfish the acanthurid will probably fool most local predators and give it the freedom to get to the food source. The mimic often follows its model around at a short distance, doing quick grazing stops along the way. The angelfishes have a moderately large territory that increases with age and it enables the mimic surgeonfish to cover large sections of reefs that are avoided by most other juvenile *Acanthurus* spp.

The surgeonfish grows much larger than the pygmy angelfish and changes its look to a more typical *Acanthurus* species when it out-grows its model, changing colour as well as the shape of its tail from rounded to strongly lunate. In the case of *Acanthurus pyroferus* all the different mimics change into the same looking adult.

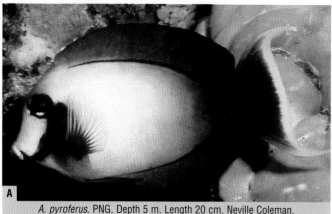

A

A. pyroferus. PNG. Depth 5 m. Length 20 cm. Neville Coleman.

Pacific Mimic Surgeon
Acanthurus pyroferus

Hepatus pyroferus. Kittlitz, 1834. Caroline I. Pacific.

Widespread Indo-West Pacific. Coastal to outer reef crests. Juveniles usually mimic various sympatric pygmy angelfishes in colour and shape (see opposite page). The form shown in **E** appears to be a non-mimic that occurs in various part of the Pacific and eastern Australia. The individual in **C** is similar to this form, but also resembles the *vrolikii*-mimic. The tail changes from rounded to lunate when outgrowing the size of the model and changes colour to that of the adult. Length to 20 cm.

See previous page on mimicry.

B

A. pyroferus. Bali, Indonesia. D. 4 m. L. 11 cm. Takamasa Tonozuka.

C

A. pyroferus. Indonesia. D. 7 m. L. 40 mm.

D

A. pyroferus. Bali, Indonesia. Depth 5 m. Length 18 cm.

E *A. pyroferus*. Vanuatu. D. 10 m. L. 40 mm. Fenton Walsh.

F *A. pyroferus*. Kerama, Japan. D. 6 m. L. 50 mm.

G MIMIC *A. pyroferus*. NSW, Australia D. 4 m. L. 40 mm.

H MODEL *Centropyge heraldi*. Sulawesi, Indonesia. D. 20 m. L. 50 mm.

I MIMIC *A. pyroferus*. Tuvalu, South Pacific. D. 5 m. L. 45 mm.

J MODEL *Centropyge flavissimus*. Micronesia. D. 4 m. L. 12 cm.

K MIMIC *A. pyroferus*. Mabul, Malaysia. D. 6 m. L. 5 cm.

L MODEL *Centropyge vrolikii*. Bali, Indonesia. D. 10 m. L. 12 cm.

A. *triostegus*. Maldives. Depth 1 m. Length 20 cm.

Convict Surgeon *Acanthurus triostegus*

Chaetodon triostegus Linnnaeus, 1758. Indies.

Widespread Indo-Pacific, but several geographical variations. Coastal reefs and estuaries. Sometimes form large schools in harbours or to feed in areas with aggressive damselfishes, which are then completely overwhelmed by their numbers. Often feeding near freshwater run-offs where certain algae grows on rocks that are grazed. Readily identified by the pale colour and distinctive pattern of vertical black bars. The black mark in front of the pectoral fin-base is variable from a spot or short dash in most populations, but forms a line in the Hawaiian form (**C**). Latter is regarded as subspecies *Acanthurus triostegus sandvicensis* by some authors. Length to 26 cm.

A. *triostegus*. Bali, Indonesia. Depth 3 m. Length 20 cm.

A. *triostegus*. Hawaii. Adult. Doug Perrine.

A. *triostegus*. Cook Islands, South Pacific. Depth 6 m. Length to 24 cm.

E

A. triostegus, spawning colours. Cocos Islands, eastern Pacific. Length about 25 cm. Peter Kragh.

F

A. triostegus. Sea of Cortez, Mexico. Depth 3 m. Length 23 cm.

Barred Surgeon *Acanthurus polyzona*

Rhombotides polyzona Bleeker, 1868.
Mayotte I., Comoro Is.; Réunion Island.

Only known from the type-localities in the western Indian Ocean near Madagascar. Juveniles are found in shallow lagoons and adults mix and feed with *Acanthurus triostegus*, scraping algae off rocks or rubble. *A. polyzona* favour high energy zones and congregate on outer reef shelves. It is readily identified by the colour pattern of many vertical dark bars. Length to 20 cm.

A. polyzona. Réunion. Depth 4 m. Length 16 cm. Alain Dirringer.

Acanthurus guttatus Forster, 1802. Tahiti.

Widespread Indo-West Pacific, but mainly occurs in oceanic locations. Usually found schooling in shallow depths over reef flats that are subject to surge or currents. A deep-bodied species that is easily identified by colour. The numerous white spots are thought to serve as camouflage when swimming near breaking waves where surface waters mix with small air-bubbles. Length to 26 cm.

See spawning on pages 22–23

A. guttatus. Solomon Islands. Depth 2 m. Length 25 cm. Bob Halstead.

A. *guttatus*. Sulawesi, Indonesia. Depth 1 m. Length 20 cm. Takamasa Tonozuka.

Acanthurus grammoptilus Richardson, 1843.
Port Essington, Northern Territory, Australia.

Appears to be restricted to tropical Australian waters, doubtful reports from elsewhere. Occurs on shallow inshore reefs, often silty habitats to about 10 m depth, usually in small groups. Has distinctive white band across base of caudal fin and body has a pattern of fine horizontal lines. Distinguished from other similar species by the colour combination of body and fins, body depth, head profile, and markings around eyes that are diagnostic. Length to 35 cm.

A. *grammoptilus*. **A** Dampier, W.A. Length 20 m. Neville Coleman. **B** Cassini Reef. W.A. Length 30 cm. Jerry Allen.

White-fin Surgeon
Acanthurus albipectoralis

Acanthurus albipectoralis.
Allen & Ayling, 1987. Coral Sea.

Coral sea to eastern Australia and Tonga. Occurs mainly in current-prone habitats, on clear coastal reef slopes, reef channels and outer reef walls. Adults in loose groups, usually in open water feeding on zooplankton. Juveniles in shallow rocky habitats feeding on algae. Adults pale grey to blue, dark band over eyes and broad white margin on pectoral fin. Very small juveniles pale bluish grey with faint dusky lines. Length to 35 cm.

A

A. albipectoralis. Coral Sea. Depth 5 m. Length 30 cm. Jerry Allen.

B

A. albipectoralis. Sydney, Australia. Depth 2 m. Length 35 mm.

C

A. albipectoralis. Sydney, Australia. Depth 3 m. Length 45 mm.

D

A. albipectoralis. Sydney, Australia. Depth 4 m. Length 15 cm.

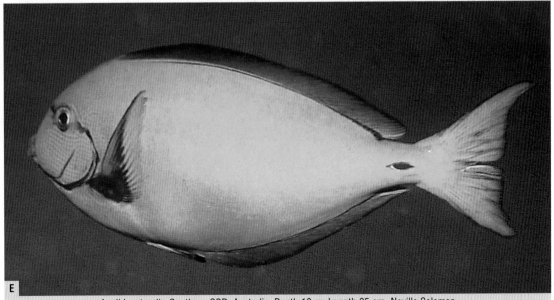

E

A. albipectoralis. Southern GBR, Australia. Depth 10 m. Length 35 cm. Neville Coleman.

A. thompsoni. Maldives. Depth 10 m. Length 22 cm.

Night Surgeonfish *Acanthurus thompsoni*

Hepatus thompsoni Fowler, 1923. Hawaii.

Widespread Indo-West Pacific. Coastal slopes to outer reef walls, usually at a depth of 20 m or more. Occurs alone or in small groups. Easily identified by the dark body and white tail. Has a black spot at the end of the base of the dorsal fin that is only obvious when the body pales, such as when visiting a cleaning station. Length to 25 cm.

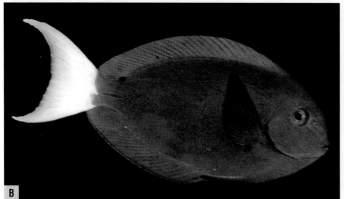

A. thompsoni. Flores, Indonesia. Depth 20 m. Length 15 cm.

A. thompsoni. Bali. D. 20 m. L. 10 cm.

A. thompsoni, with juvenile *Bodianus diana* working as a cleaner, removing parasites. Maldives. Depth 10 m. Length 22 cm.

Pin-striped Surgeon *Acanthurus nubilus*

Hepatus nubilus Fowler & Bean, 1929. Sulawesi.

Widespread Indo-West Pacific. Usually found along deep outer reef walls. Rarely noticed by divers because of the lack of distinctive features. Identified by the numerous thin lines along the body, dorsal and anal fins. Length to 25 cm.

A. *nubilus.* **A** Cook Is, South Pacific. Depth 25 m. Length 75 mm. **B** Guam. Depth 35 m. Length 22 cm.

A. *nubilus.* **C** Cook Is, South Pacific. Depth 25 m. Length 75 mm. **D** Solomon I. Depth 20 m. Length 24 cm. Neville Coleman.

A. nubilus. Flores, Indonesia. D. 30 m. L. 20 cm.

A. nubilus. Flores, Indonesia. Depth 30 m. Length 20 cm.

A

A. auranticavus. Sulawesi, Indonesia. D. 5 m. L. 15 cm. Jerry Allen.

Ring-tail Surgeon
Acanthurus auranticavus

Acanthurus auranticavus. Randall, 1956.
Philippines.

Widespread Indo-Pacific. Shallow coastal to outer reef crest and slopes. Adults in groups, often mixed with other similar species. Identified by the vertical white band on the base of the caudal fin and short angled dark band, like joined elongated spots, behind the eye. Sometimes shows a rusty-orange colour surrounding the peduncular spines (**C**) and alternating pale and dark bands on the chest. Length to 45 cm.

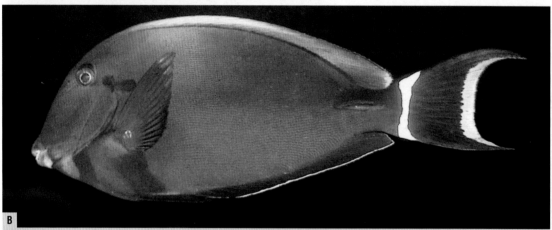

B

A. auranticavus. Bali, Indonesia. Depth 8 m. Length 45 cm.

C

A. auranticavus. Bali, Indonesia. Depth 8 m. Length 45 cm.

Monk Surgeonfish
Acanthurus gahhm

Chaetodon nigrofuscus var. *gahhm.*
Forsskål, 1775. Red Sea.

Red Sea and Gulf of Aden, Arabian Sea.
Usually found over open sand and rubble
bottom in lagoons or at the base of seaward
reefs. Occurs in small groups or forms large,
loose aggregations. Similar to *Acanthurus
nigricaudus* and is best distinguished from it
by the lack of a black stripe in front of the
spine. Length to 40 cm.

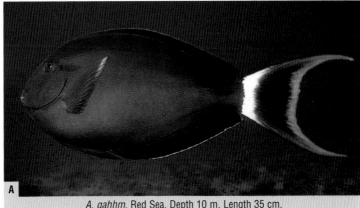

A

A. gahhm. Red Sea. Depth 10 m. Length 35 cm.

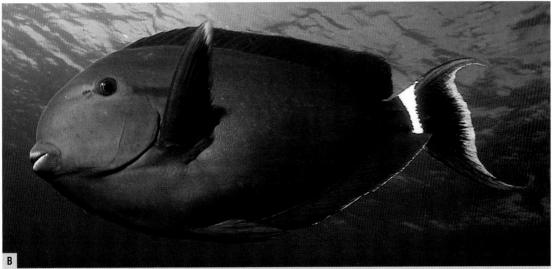

B

A. gahhm. Red Sea. Depth 5 m. Length 40 cm.

C

A. gahhm. Red Sea. Depth 15 m. Length 30–40 cm.

Acanthurus gahm var *nigricauda*
Duncker & Mohr, 1929.
Bismarck Archipelago.

Widespread Indo-West Pacific. Occurs on shallow coastal to outer reef slopes, usually swimming with groups of mixed acanthurid species. A distinctly coloured species. Adults are easily identified by the long tail and the long black line behind the eye, as well as a black line running anteriorly from peduncular spine. Length to 45 cm.

A. nigricaudus. Bali, Indonesia. Depth 3 m. Length 40 cm.

A. nigricaudus. Uepi. Solomon Islands. Depth 7 m. Length 45 cm. Neville Coleman.

A. nigricaudus. Bali, Indonesia. Depth 3 m. Length 45 cm.

A. nigricaudus. Seychelles. Depth 9 m. Length 45 cm. Neville Coleman.

A. nigricaudus on the left, with *A. leucocheilos* on the right. Bali, Indonesia. Depth 4 m. Length 45 cm.

A. nigricaudus, aggregation accompanied by *Ctenochaetus striatus*. Maldives. Depth 4 m. Length 45 cm.

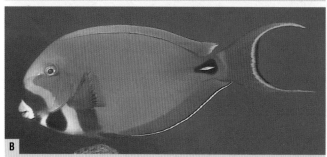

Acanthurus leucocheilus. Herre, 1927. Philippines.
Acanthurus melanosternon. Smith, 1955. Aldabra.

Widespread Indo-West Pacific. Shallow protected reef flats and slopes to outer reef walls. Highly variable in colour and adults are best identified by their dark colour (usually) and white spine. Adults regularly show a white vertical band on caudal fin base, mostly when feeding, some individuals have a completely white caudal fin, and juveniles usually have a yellow-white caudal fin. Length to 45 cm.

A. leucocheilus. Seychelles. Depth 7 m. Length 35 cm.

A. leucocheilus. Maldives. Depth 15 m. Length 45 cm. Neville Coleman.

A. leucocheilus. Bali, Indonesia. D. 5 m. L. 18 cm.

A. leucocheilus. Maldives. Depth 15 m. Length 45 cm. Neville Coleman.

E

A. leucocheilus. Andaman Sea. D. 9 m. L. 45 cm.

A. leucocheilus. Seychelles. Depth 7 m. Length 45 cm. Neville Coleman.

Dark Surgeon *Acanthurus blochii*

Acanthurus blochii. Valenciennes, 1835. Mauritius.

Widespread Indo-Pacific. Outer reef habitats from shallow lagoons to deep slopes. Usually seen in small groups and may school in some oceanic locations. Adults are distinguished from similar species by their bluish black median fins, a caudal fin which is often deep-blue, and a yellowish spot behind the eye. Length to 45 cm.

A. *blochii*. GBR, Australia. **A** Depth 10 m. Length 20 cm. Kendall Clements. **B** Depth 20 m. Length 40 cm. Neville Coleman.

A. blochii. Iriomote I., Japan. Depth 25 m. Length 40 cm.

A. blochii. Great Barrier Reef, Australia. Depth 20 m. Length 45 cm. Neville Coleman.

Acanthurus dussumieri.
Valenciennes, 1835. Mauritius.

Widespread Indo-Pacific, Africa to Hawaii. Adults mainly on deep coastal reef slopes and outer reef walls, often on deep shipwrecks. Juveniles coastal on algae-rocky reef. Distinguished by the white peduncular spine from the very similar *A. blochii* and *A. xanthopterus*. Juveniles dusky with yellowish dorsal fin and pale whitish tail. Length to 50 cm.

A. dussumieri. Maldives. Depth 25 m. Length 45 cm.

A. dussumieri. **B – D** NSW, Australia. Depth 2-3 m. Lengths: **B** 15 cm, **C** 10 cm, & **D** 5 cm.

A. dussumieri. Great Barrier Reef, Australia. Depth 30 m. Length 45 cm. Phil Woodhead.

Eye-spot Surgeon *Acanthurus bariene*

Acanthurus bariene. Lesson, 1831. Waigeo.

Widespread Indo-Pacific. Adults mainly on deep coastal reef slopes and outer reef walls. A distinctly coloured species. Adults are identified by the yellow around the eyes and the eye-sized blue-black spot closely behind. Dorsal fin yellow with blue line along its base. Large adults have a strongly rounded snout profile. Length to 45 cm.

A. bariene. Bali, Indonesia. Depth 5 m. Length 35 cm.

A. bariene. Maldives. Depth 20 m. Length 40 cm.

A. bariene. Bali, Indonesia. Depth 6 m. Length 40 cm.

Yellow-mask Surgeon
Acanthurus xanthopterus

Acanthurus xanthopterus
Valenciennes, 1835. Seychelles.

Widespread Indo-West Pacific. Various reef habitats, sand slopes and lagoons, and juveniles often in estuaries. Adults usually in aggregations feeding on sand and rubble surfaces. Capable of enormous colour changes, hence very similar to *A. dussumieri* and *A. blochii*, but always distinct by yellow pextoral fins. Juveniles with white lines on dorsal and anal fin. Length to 50 cm.

A. *xanthopterus*. Bali, Indonesia. Depth 10 m. Length 45 cm.

C

A. *xanthopterus*. Hawaii.

D

A. *xanthopterus*. Flores, Indonesia. Depth 6 m. Length 15 cm.

A. *xanthopterus*. Java. D. 2 m. L. 9 cm.

A. *xanthopterus*, feeding on detritus and algae-growth on the sand surface. Maldives. Depth 18 m. Length 45 cm.

52

Pale Surgeon
Acanthurus mata

Acanthurus mata. Cuvier, 1829.
Acanthurus bleekeri. Günther, 1861.
No localities.

Widespread Indo-Pacific. Occurs on coastal to outer reef crest and slopes. Adults often seen in schools, feeding mid-water on plankton. Identified by the pale grey or blue body and yellow 'mask'. Juveniles with a distinctive horizontal-lined pattern of alternating pale-blue and dusky lines. Peduncular spine black in adults. Length to 45 cm.

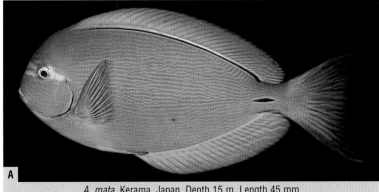

A

A. mata. Kerama, Japan. Depth 15 m. Length 45 mm.

B *A. mata.* Bali. D. 5 m. L. 40 mm. T. Tonozuka.

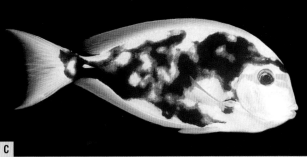

C *A. mata.* Abberrantion. Maldives. Herwarth Voigtmann.

D *A. mata.* Bali, Indonesia. D. 5 m. L. 45 mm.

E *A. mata.* Bali, Indonesia. Depth 20 m. Length 40 cm.

F *A. mata.* Schooling adults. Maldives. Depth 10 m. Length ~40 cm.

53

Acanthurus fowleri. de Beaufort, 1951. Based on *Acanthurus pyroferus* Fowler & Bean, 1929. Philippines.

Widespread West Pacific. Occurs mainly on deep coastal reef slopes and outer reef walls, usually in small groups and at moderate depths of about 20 m or more. A distinctly coloured species. Adults are easily identified by the mostly blue head and horse-shoe mark above the pectoral fin base. Length to 45 cm.

A. fowleri. Flores, Indonesia. Depth 25 m. Length 45 cm.

A. fowleri. Milne Bay, PNG. Depth 15 m. Length 35 cm.

A. fowleri. Sulawesi, Indonesia. Depth 20 m. Length 40 cm.

Spot-face Surgeon
Acanthurus maculiceps

Hepatus maculiceps. Ahl, 1923. Melanesia.

Widespread Indo-West Pacific. Shallow, often exposed coastal to outer reef flats. Usually in schools of mixed similar species when grazing algae. Adults easily identified by the numerous pale spots over the head and the yellow-tipped pectoral fin. Length to 40 cm.

A. maculiceps. **A** Iriomote, Japan. Depth 6 m. Length 40 cm. **B** Bali, Indonesia. Depth 3 m. Length 40 cm.

A. maculiceps. Bali, Indonesia. Depth 3 m. Length 40 cm.

A. maculiceps. Bali, Indonesia. Depth 3 m. Length 40 cm.

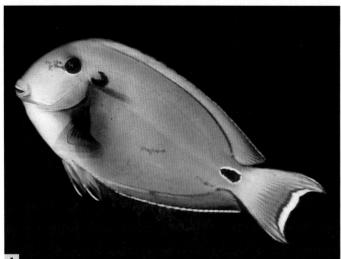

Acanthurus tennentii Günther, 1861. Sri Lanka.

Widespread Indian Ocean, ranging to Bali where it mixes with *Acanthurus olivaceus*. Occurs in small groups on reef flats and slopes. Identified by the bluish black colour, peduncular spine surrounded by black with blue edge, and a black mark above pectoral fin base that develops into short, double stripes. Juveniles black to yellow body, yellow caudal fin and dark eye. Length to 31 cm.

A
A. tennentii. Bali, Indonesia. Depth 8 m. Length 15 cm.

B

C
A. tennentii. Bali, Indonesia. **B** Length. 6 cm. Takamasa Tonozuka. **C** Depth 12 m. Length 30 cm.

D
A. tennentii. Mahe I, Seychelles. Depth 12 m. Length 30 cm. Neville Coleman.

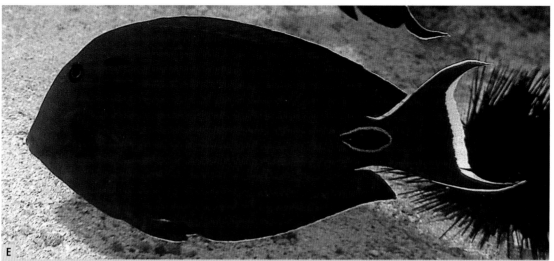

A. tennentii. Seychelles, Indian Ocean. Depth 10 m. Length 30 cm.

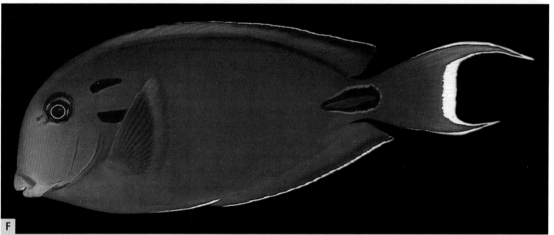

A. tennentii. Maldives, Indian Ocean. Depth 20 m. Length 30 cm.

A. tennentii. Sodwana Bay, South Africa. Depth 12 m. Length 31 cm. Dennis King.

Orange-blotch Surgeon
Acanthurus olivaceus

Acanthurus olivaceus
Bloch & Schneider, 1801. Tahiti.

Widespread West to Central Pacific, ranging to sub-tropical zones as juveniles during summer. Coastal reef slopes and inner reefs, usually in small groups on sand and rubble zones. Juveniles in shallow coastal bays in rocky habitats. Adults grey-yellow to almost black, often posterior half abruptly darker, and featuring a bright orange blotch behind eye. Small juveniles bright yellow and blue anal fin margin. Length to 35 cm.

A. olivaceus. GBR, Australia. Depth 20 m. Length 30 cm. Neville Coleman.

A. olivaceus. **B** GBR, Australia. Depth 10 m. Length 12 cm. Phil Woodhead. **C** Sydney, Australia. Depth 3 m. Length 45 mm.

A. olivaceus. Bali, Indonesia. Depth 5 m. Length 35 cm.

A. olivaceus. Cook Islands, South Pacific. Depth 7 m. Adults.

A. olivaceus. Hawaiian Islands. Depth 10 m. Length 30 cm.

A. olivaceus. Hawaiian Islands. Depth 22 m. Length 30 cm.

Arabian Surgeon
Acanthurus sohal

Chaetodon sohal. Forsskål, 1775. Red Sea.

Only occurs in the Red Sea, Arabian Sea and Arabian Gulf. Along outer edge of reef-flats to about 10 m depth. Juveniles and often adults are solitary and territorial, but occur also in small groups. Easily identified by the numerous black lines on the body in all stages. Peduncular spine is thought to be venomous. Length to 40 cm.

A. sohal. Red Sea. Depth 6 m. Length 40 cm. Hugues Vitry.

A. sohal. **B** & **C** Oman, Phil Woodhead. Length **B** 40 cm, **C** 50 mm. **D** Egypt, Red Sea Depth 1 m. Length 10 cm.

A. sohal. Egypt, Red Sea. Depth 7 m. Length 40 cm.

F *A. sohal*. Red Sea. Reef crests that are exposed to surge have good algae growth and crevices, providing food and shelter.

G *A. sohal*. Red Sea. Reef crests appear to be the preferred habitat for this species where it is often seen in loose groups.

Lined Surgeon
Acanthurus lineatus

Chaetodon lineatus. Linnaeus, 1756. Indies.

Widespread Indo-West Pacific. Shallow coastal to outer reef flats, often in exposed reefs subject to surge. Adults usually form schools and are commonly found in shallow reef-gutters. Juveniles solitary and secretive on shallow rubble habitats. Readily identified by the orange and blue lined pattern. Peduncular spine is venomous. Length to 35 cm. Also known as Blue-lined Surgeonfish.

A. lineatus. **A** Bali, Indonesia. Depth 6 m. Length 35 cm. **B** Seal Rocks, NSW, Australia. Depth 2 m. Length 55 mm.

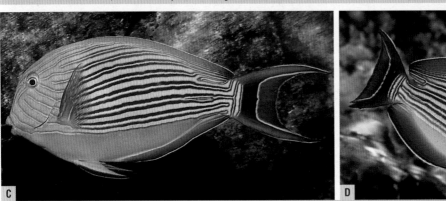

A. lineatus. **C** Maldives. Depth 4 m. Length 35 cm. **D** Iriomote I., Japan. Depth 3 m. Length 10 cm.

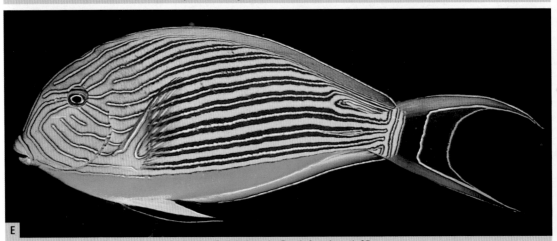

A. lineatus. Bali, Indonesia. Depth 6 m. Length 35 cm.

Dusky Surgeonfish *Acanthurus nigrofuscus*

Cheatodon nigrofuscus Forskåll, 1775. Red Sea.

Widespread Indo-West Pacific. Usually occurs in algae-rocky habitats. Coastal reefs and harbours to outer reef gutters and channels to about 20 m depth. Adults usually in small groups, but form large schools in some oceanic locations. Juveniles are often seen feeding with mixed species aggregations. Adults identified by the small orange spots on their head, blue to mauve tail and a dark spot at the end of the anal and dorsal fin-base. Juveniles brown to bluish black when small, and the head with orange scribbles that break up into spots with growth. Length to 20 cm.

A. *nigrofuscus*. Egypt, Red Sea. Depth 7 m. Length 16 cm.

B. *A. nigrofuscus*. Sydney, Australia. Depth 6 m. L. 45 mm.

C. *A. nigrofuscus*. Egypt, Red Sea. Depth 6 m. Length 5 cm.

D. *A. nigrofuscus*. Micronesia. Depth 10 m. Length 15 cm.

E. *A. nigrofuscus*. Kerama, Japan. Depth 15 m. Length 15 cm.

F. *A. nigrofuscus*. Flores, Indonesia. Depth 20 m. Length 15 cm.

G. *A. nigrofuscus*. Bali, Indonesia. Depth 6 m. Length 15 cm.

monroviae 64

bahianus 65

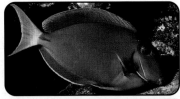

bahianus 65

coeruleus 66

chirurgus 68

chirurgus 68

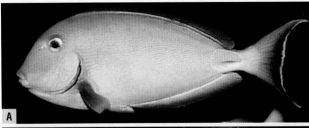

West African Tang *Acanthurus monroviae*

Acanthurus monroviae. Steindachner, 1876. Liberia.

Tropical eastern Atlantic from Morocco to Angola, Cape Verde Island, São Tomé. Occurs on coastal reefs and enters estuaries and lagoons. Reported from 20–200 m depth. This species is readily identified by the bright yellow patch on the caudal peduncle, highlighting its defensive spine. Length to 30 cm.

A. monroviae. Cape Verde Islands, eastern Atlantic. **C** juvenile, other photographs depict adults. Peter Wirtz.

Ocean Tang *Acanthurus bahianus*

Acanthurus bahianus. Castelnau, 1855. Brazil.

Known from Ascension, St. Helena, and tropical western Atlantic with stragglers north to Massachusetts and south to Rio de Janeiro. Mainly found on hard substrates grazing on algae. Shallow reefs to about 25 m depth. Grey-yellow to brown with thin longitudinal lines on the dorsal fin and along the sides of the body, latter especially noticeable in young. Length to 36 cm, commonly to 25 cm.

A. *A. bahianus*. Florida. Juvenile. Aquarium.

B. *A. bahianus*. Bahamas, western Atlantic. Depth 8 m. Length 25 cm. Doug Perrine.

E. *A. bahianus*. Bonaire. Netherlands Antilles. **C** & **D** about 15 cm, **D** night. **E** large school grazing algae. Otto Gremblewski.

Blue Tang *Acanthurus coeruleus*

Chaetodon coeruleus. Bloch & Schneider, 1801.
Carolinas, Havana & Jamaica.

Tropical western Atlantic and Ascension Islands.
Stragglers north to New York and south to Rio de Janeiro.
Occurs on shallow reefs, ranging to about 25 m depth, and
swims singly or in small aggregations. Often mixes with
schooling *Acanthurus chirurgus* or *A. bahianus*. Adult *A.
coeruleus* are bluer, and deeper bodied than the other two
species. The peduncular spine is white or yellow. Small
juveniles are mostly bright yellow. Length to 35 cm.

A. coeruleus. Bimini, Bahamas, western Atlantic.Depth 6 m. L. 30 cm.

A. coeruleus. Curacao. D. 7 m. L. 4 cm.

A. coeruleus. Florida Keys. Depth 10 m. Length 8 cm. Roger Steene.

A. coeruleus. Florida Keys. Night. Doug Perrine.

A. coeruleus. Curacao, Netherlands Antilles, western Atlantic. Depth 10 m. Length 20 cm.

A. coeruleus. **F** Bonaire, feeding amongst corals. Otto Gremblewski. **G** Caribbean, feeding in a bed of seagrass. Doug Perrine.

Chaetodon chirurgus. Bloch, 1787. West Indies.

Tropical western Atlantic with stragglers north to Massachusetts and south to Rio de Janeiro, and tropical West Africa, Senegal. It is mainly common on shallow rocky reefs of the West Indies. Identified by its grey to brown colour with about 10 narrow dusky bars on the sides above the anal fin, and the bright blue edge to the peduncular spine. Length to 35 cm, but commonly to 25 cm.

A

A. chirurgus. Bonaire, western Atlantic. D. 15 m. L. 30 cm. Otto Gremblewski.

B

A. chirurgus. Antigua, western Atlantic. Depth 15 m. Length 22 cm.

C

A. chirurgus, schooling, with a single *A. coeruleus* (centre, background) and *A. bahianus* (right, front). Apart from the general colouration, each species can be distinguished by the different tail-spine colours. Bonaire, western Atlantic. Otto Gremblewski.

GENUS *Paracanthurus* Bleeker, 1863

Masculine. Type species: *Teuthis hepatus* Bloch & Schneider (not of Linnaeus) 1801. Monotypic genus, closely related to *Acanthurus* and readily separated from that genus in having only 3 versus 5 rays in the ventral fin. A wide-ranging species found on coral reefs throughout the Indo-West Pacific. Some geographical variations.

Behaviour
As for *Acanthurus* (see page 20), but feeds primarily on zooplankton as a juvenile, combining diet with benthic algae as an adult.

Characteristics of the genus *Paracanthurus*.
Oval body, depth about 2.4 times in SL; caudal peduncle compressed, depth about 2.5 times in head length; dorsal-fin spines usually IX; anal-fin spines III; ventral fin I, 3; teeth on jaws fixed, incurved, thin and wide with denticulate edges; upper teeth fewer than 26; scales with ctenii on posterior margins.

Blue Surgeonfish *Paracanthurus hepatus*

Teuthis hepatus Linnaeus, 1766. Ambon.

Widespread Indo-West Pacific, but west Indian Ocean population considerably different. Coastal to outer reef flats subject to currents and surge, often very shallow and usually in depths of less than 10 m. Juveniles secretive in *Acropora* thickets, swimming just above to feed on plankton. Large adults swim about openly and graze algae, sometimes forming schools to feed on plankton. Length reported to 26 cm, but usually to 20 cm in the West Pacific.

A

P. hepatus. Bali, Indonesia. Depth 5 m. Length 40 mm.

B

P. hepatus. Bali, Indonesia. Depth 3 m. Length 16 cm.

C

P. hepatus. Bali, Indonesia. Depth 4 m. Length 16 cm.

69

P. hepatus. Maldives. Depth 4 m. Length 24 cm.

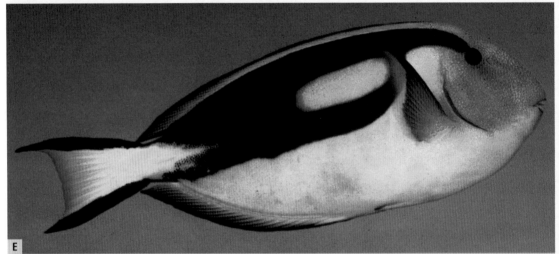

P. hepatus. Mauritius. Depth 4 m. Length 26 cm.

P. hepatus. Seychelles. Depth 4 m. Length 24 cm. Neville Coleman.

G *P. hepatus.* Flores, Indonesia. Schooling juveniles on reef crest. They feed primarily on zooplankton at this stage.

H *P. hepatus.* Bali, Indonesia. Adults taking shelter amongst corals. These were observed grazing on algae.

GENUS *Ctenochaetus* Gill, 1884

Masculine. Type species: *Acanthurus strigosus* Bennett 1828. Comprises at least 6 species, possibly 10. At this stage it is not clear if certain members of species-complex represent valid species, are sub-specific, or are actually regional colour morphs of a single taxon. The species in *Ctenochaetus* are superficially similar in appearance to those in *Acanthurus,* but are distinguished from that genus by having a different jaw structure and having flexible and more numerous teeth. All species have 8 dorsal-fin spines compared to the usual 9 count in *Acanthurus* (only *A. pyroferus* & A. *tristis* have 8).

Behaviour
As for *Acanthurus* (see page 20), but the *Ctenochaetus* feed on detritus, a thin film of matter on the substrate that may contain high concentrations of simple unicellular algae, which is scooped up from the sand or scraped from hard surfaces.

Characteristics of the genus *Ctenochaetus*.
Oval body, depth about 2 times in SL; caudal peduncle compressed, depth about 2.5 times in head length; dorsal-fin spines VIII (first small and easily overlooked); anal-fin spines III; ventral fin I, 5; teeth on jaws movable, incurved, attenuate with incurved and denticulate tips; upper teeth more than 30; scales with ctenii on posterior margins.

Ctenochaetus Picture Index

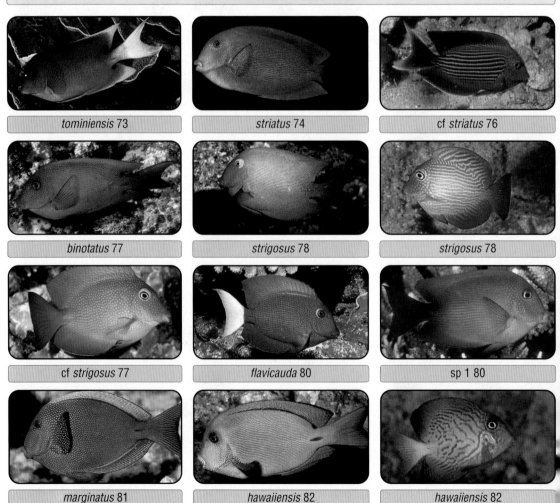

tominiensis 73	*striatus* 74	cf *striatus* 76
binotatus 77	*strigosus* 78	*strigosus* 78
cf *strigosus* 77	*flavicauda* 80	sp 1 80
marginatus 81	*hawaiiensis* 82	*hawaiiensis* 82

Yellow-tip Bristletooth
Ctenochaetus tominiensis

Ctenochaetus tominiensis Randall, 1960.
Sulawesi, Indonesia Is.

West Pacific, from Palau and Philippines to Indonesia, Solomon Islands and northern Great Barrier Reef. Occurs mainly in pristine outer reef habitats with rich coral growth. Easily identified by the orange-tipped dorsal and anal fins that look bright yellow in natural light. Length to 16 cm.

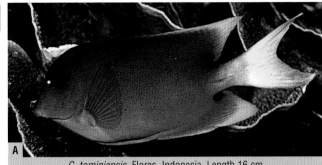

A

C. tominiensis. Flores, Indonesia. Length 16 cm.

B

C. tominiensis. Mabul, Malaysia. Length 35 mm.

C

C. tominiensis. Flores, Indonesia. Length 16 cm.

D

C. tominiensis. Flores, Indonesia. Length ~5 cm.

E

C. tominiensis. Cleaned by wrasses. Flores, Indonesia. Length ~12 cm.

F

C. tominiensis. Flores, Indonesia. Typical habitat, rich in corals and algae. Depth 25 m. Length 15 cm.

Fine-lined Bristletooth
Ctenochaetus striatus

Acanthurus striatus Quoy & Gaimard, 1825. Guam, Mariana Is.

Widespread Indo-West Pacific, but some geographical variations. Pectoral fin bright yellow in the Red Sea. A common species in most areas, often forming large schools in oceanic locations. It combs organic detritus from reef surfaces, especially in shallow habitats subject to surge. Also found on inner reefs and in lagoons to about 20 m depth. Identified by the numerous fine lines along the body, and the small orange spots on its head. Length to 25 cm.

C. striatus. Kerama, Japan. Depth 5 m. Length 20 cm.

C. striatus. Bali, Indonesia. Depth 3 m. Length 22 cm.

C. striatus. Juvenile, aquarium. Length 40 mm.

C. striatus. Egypt, Red Sea. Depth 3 m. Length 22 cm.

C. striatus. Maldives. Depth 3 m. Length 22 cm.

C. striatus. Nuptial colour. Maldives. Depth 5 m. Length 20 cm.

C. striatus. Nuptial colour. Maldives. Depth 5 m. Length 20 cm.

C. striatus. Guam (type-locality), Micronesia. Depth 20 m. Length 24 cm.

C. striatus. Egypt, Red Sea. Depth 15 m. Length 22 cm.

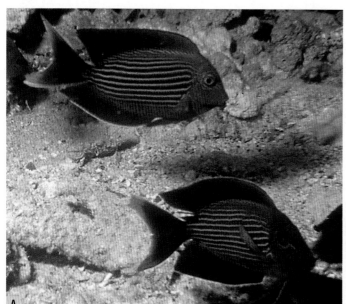

Orange-lined Bristletooth
Ctenochaetus cf *striatus*

Uncertain status

Indo-West Pacific, known from Maldives and Sri Lanka to the Pacific. This form or colour-morph is usually referred to as the juvenile stage of *Ctenochaetus striatus*. However, the head of *C. striatus* has numerous small yellow to orange spots, even when juvenile, and if these are lacking in this form, it needs further investigation. It occurs in silty coastal habitats, as well as along outer reef slopes, sometimes forming large schools. Identified by the 10–12 bright orange lines and irridescent blue fin margins. Length to about 20 cm.

C. cf *striatus*. Sri Lanka. Depth 10 m. Length 10 cm.

C. cf *striatus*. Aquarium. Length 45 mm.

C. cf *striatus*. Schooling juveniles, Tuvalu, South Pacific. Depth 10 m. Length 10 cm.

C. cf *striatus*. Schooling adults, Maldives. Depth 10 m. Length ~20 cm. Helmut Corneli.

Two-spot Bristletooth
Ctenochaetus binotatus

Ctenochaetus binotatus Randall, 1955. Philippines.

Widespread Indo-West Pacific. Various reef habitats, occurring singly, in pairs or small groups. Identified by the dark spots opposite each other at the ends of the dorsal and anal fin bases, usually with yellow shadowing behind. Eye distinctly blue. Caudal fin yellow in most small juveniles and adults in some populations, depending on locality. Length to about 20 cm, but usually smaller.

A

C. binotatus. Pulau Putri, Java, Indonesia. Length 18 cm.

B

C. binotatus. GBR, Australia. L. 35 mm.

D

C. binotatus. Bali, Indonesia. Length 20 cm.

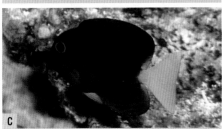

C

C. binotatus. GBR, Australia. Phil Woodhead.

E

C. binotatus. Sangehi I., Indonesia. L. 45 mm.

F

C. binotatus. Flores, Indonesia. Length 18 cm.

G

C. binotatus. Flores, Indonesia. Length 55 mm.

H

C. binotatus. GBR, Australia. Length 75 mm. Neville Coleman.

Hawaiian Gold-ring Bristletooth
Ctenochaetus strigosus

Acanthurus strigosus Bennett, 1828.
Hawaiian Is.

Appears to be endemic to the Hawaiian Islands. Various shallow reef habitats, often in small aggregations. The name has been broadly used throughout the Indo-Pacific for several other species. This species is distinctive in colouration as juvenile and the bright yellow eyes show particularly in the darker adults. A common species in the Hawaiian Islands, reaching a length of 18 cm

C. strigosus. Midway, Hawaiian Islands. Large adult. Kendall Clements.

C. strigosus. Hawaii. Juvenile (**B**) and juvenile with adult and cleaner wrasse (**C**).

C. strigosus. Hawaii. Schooling.

Indian Gold-ring Bristletooth
Ctenochaetus cf *strigosus*

An undescribed species, previously misidentified as *Ctenochaetus strigosus*. Widespread Indian Ocean from African coast to Andaman Sea and West Java. Occurs in clear inner reef crests and slopes, often in small aggregations, usually in less than 15 m depth. Readily identified by the bright yellow around the eye and the numerous pale spots all over the head and body. Juveniles are usually bright yellow with irridescent blue margins on dorsal and anal fins. Length to 18 cm.

C. cf *strigosus*. Maldives. Depth 8 m. Length 15 cm.

C. cf *strigosus*. **B** Maldives. Juvenile about 50 mm. **C** Aldabra. Length 18 cm.

C. cf *strigosus*. Seychelles. Adults.

White-tail Bristletooth
Ctenochaetus flavicauda

Acanthurus flavicauda Fowler, 1938. Tuamotu Island.

Known from south-eastern Pacific and a variation in the south-western Pacific. Previously included with *Ctenochaetus strigosus*. Small juveniles are yellow but usually change to a dark colour at about 45 mm length. It has spots on the head and lines along the body, similar to *C.* sp 1, but the eye is shaded with yellow along the back. Mouth has bluish lips. The caudal fin of the adult is white in the eastern region of the south Pacific, but as a continuation of the body colouration in the western region. Length to 14 cm.

A

C. flavicauda. Cook Islands, South Pacific. Depth 10 m. Adult, about 12 cm.

B

C. cf *flavicauda.* Qld, Australia. Kendall Clements.

C

C. flavicauda. Cook Islands. Different juveniles

Dusky Bristletooth *Ctenochaetus* sp 1

An undescribed species, previously misidentified as *Ctenochaetus strigosus.* West Pacific, Indonesia and Philippines, but probably more widespread. Occurs on sheltered inner to outer reef habitats with rich coral growth. Usually in pairs or small groups. Juveniles solitary amongst corals. Identified by its dull appearance, fine spotting on head, longitudinal lines along the body and a bluish mouth. Caudal-fin is short, nearly truncate, in young and only becomes lunate in large adults. Small juveniles all yellow with blue in eyes. Length to 16 cm.

A

C. sp 1. Flores, Indonesia. Depth 12 m. Length 10 cm.

B

C. sp 1. Sangihe I, Indonesia. D. 8 m. L. 5 cm.

C. sp 1. Flores, Indonesia. Depth 7 m. Length 15 cm.

Spotted Bristletooth
Ctenochaetus marginatus

Acanthurus marginatus Valenciennes, 1835.
Caroline Islands.

Known from scattered localities of the western and eastern Pacific. Occurs on shallow exposed coral and rocky reefs subject to wave action. A distinctive, large species. The adults with numerous small, pale bluish-green spots over the head, body and pectoral fin. The median fins have numerous pale yellow to green longitudinal lines. Length to 22 cm.

C. marginatus. **A** & **B** Clipperton I., eastern Pacific. Jerry Allen.

Chevron Bristletooth
Ctenochaetus hawaiiensis

Ctenochaetus hawaiiensis Randall, 1955.
Hawaiian Islands.

Known from various oceanic locations of the Pacific plate, ranging from the Hawaiian Islands to Palau and south to Samoa and the Marquesas Islands. Adults occur in small groups in shallow boulder regions, whilst juveniles are seen singly in rich coral habitats. Large adults have numerous fine pale-greenish lines over the head and along the body, but appear almost black at a distance, and are known as Black Surgeon in Hawaii. Small juveniles differ markedly in having bright colours and chevron-line markings. Grows large, length to 24 cm.

C. hawaiiensis. Cook Islands, South Pacific.

C. hawaiiensis. Sub-adult in aquarium.

C. hawaiiensis. Juvenile in aquarium.

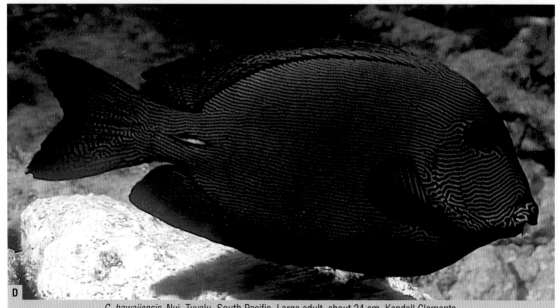

C. hawaiiensis. Nui, Tuvalu, South Pacific. Large adult, about 24 cm. Kendall Clements.

GENUS *Zebrasoma* Swainson, 1839

Neutral. Type species: *Acanthurus velifer* Bloch 1795. A distinctive genus, deep bodied with pointed snout, comprising 7 species variously distributed in the Indo-Pacific. Some are widespread, showing little variation over a large geographical area and some are localised in much smaller regions.

Behaviour

Similar to *Acanthurus* (P. 20). Species may pair or school, depending on locality and spawning behaviour. Juveniles are normally solitary and secretive in coral gardens. *Zebrasoma* species seem to be quite selective in their food. They are browsers on fleshy algae and ingest small amounts of sediment when they feed.

Characters of the genus *Zebrasoma*.
Body deeply oval and dorsal and anal fins tall, the combined height from top of dorsal fin to bottom of anal fin about equal to total length; dorsal fin spines IV or V; anal-fin spines III; ventral fin I, 5.

Zebrasoma Picture Index

veliferum 84

desjardinii 86

scopas 88

scopas 88

flavescens 90

xanthurum 92

gemmatum 94

rostratum 95

Pacific Sailfin Tang
Zebrasoma veliferum

Acanthurus velifer Bloch, 1795. East Indies.

Widespread West and Central Pacific. Replaced in the Indian Ocean by the closely related *Zebrasoma desjardinii*, west from Java. Occurs mainly on coastal reefs and sheltered inner reefs. Adults may school in some oceanic locations, but are often seen alone. Juveniles typically seen in large coral thickets and usually solitary. Readily identified by the tall fins and colouration. Length to 30 cm.

Z. veliferum. Truk Lagoon, Micronesia. Alison Kuiter.

Z. veliferum. **B** Bali, Indonesia. Large adult, night colour. **C** Kerama, Japan. Large juvenile, length about 12 cm.

Z. veliferum. Bali, Indonesia. Depth 7 m. Length 25 cm.

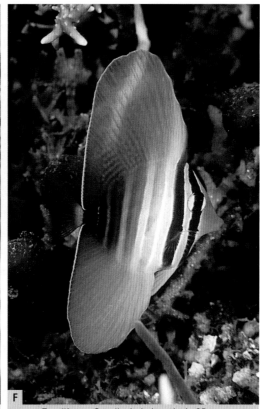

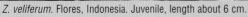
Z. *veliferum*. Flores, Indonesia. Juvenile, length about 6 cm.

Z. *veliferum*. Sangihe I., Indonesia. L. 35 mm.

Z. *veliferum*. Sangihe I., Indonesia. Depth 6 m. Length 35 mm.

Indian Sailfin Tang
Zebrasoma desjardinii

Zebrasoma desjardinii Bennett, 1828. Mauritius.

Widespread Indian Ocean and Red Sea, ranging east to west Java and replaced by the closely related *Zebrasoma veliferum* further east. Inner to outer reef flats and slopes. Adults usually in small groups and may gather in large numbers for spawning. Readily identified by their rounded appearance and colour. Some variations in colouration and patterns between different geographical zones. Length to 40 cm.

Z. desjardinii. Maldives. Depth 20 m. Large adult, about 40 cm.

Z. desjardinii. Seychelles. **B** Adult, about 30 cm and **C** juvenile about 8 cm.

Z. desjardinii. Egypt, Red Sea. **D** Adult, about 30 cm and **E** juvenile about 7 cm.

Z. desjardinii. Maldives. Depth 15 m. Large adult, about 40 cm feeding on algae from the back of a turtle. Doug Perrine.

Z. desjardinii. Red Sea. Large adults in a typical Red Sea reef scene.

A

Z. scopas. Sangihe I., Indonesia. Depth 10 m. Length 15 cm.

Brown Sailfin Tang *Zebrasoma scopas*

Acanthurus scopas Cuvier, 1829. Banda.

Widespread Indo-Pacific, but several colour forms and relationship with *Zebrasoma flavescens*, the yellow tang, and *Z. rostratum*, the black tang, is unclear. They occur together in some areas and inter-breed. Various reef habitats, inshore to outer reefs. Adults may swim in pairs, groups, or form schools in certain localities. Juveniles solitary in amongst corals. Variable in colour from nearly black-looking underwater to brown or yellow. Small juveniles with thin vertical lines. Peduncular spine white at all stages. Length to 16 cm.

Note: unusual colour patterns (**G**) in some *Zebrasoma* species are thought to be the result of a fungal infection. It starts as irregular black markings on the body, spreading over large parts of the sides and onto the fins (Dr. Kendall Clements, pers. comm.).

B

Z. scopas. Seychelles. Depth 10 m. Length 16 cm.

C

Z. scopas. Maldives. Depth 6 m. Length 5 cm.

D

Z. scopas. Flores, Indonesia. Depth 12 m. Length 10 cm.

E

Z. scopas. Maldives. Depth 6 m. Length 5 cm.

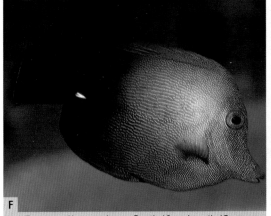

F | *Z. scopas.* Kerama, Japan. Depth 18 m. Length 15 cm.

G | *Z. scopas.* Aquarium, Philippines specimen. Fungal infection?

H | *Z. scopas.* Kerama, Japan. D. 10 m. L. 10 cm.

I | *Z. scopas.* Aquarium, Japan. Apparently it was brown when captured.

J | *Z. scopas* & *Z. flavescens*?. Kerama, Japan. Depth 16 m. At this locality the two colour forms or species mix in small groups.

A

Z. flavescens. Hawaii. Adult. Ed Robinson.

Yellow Sailfin Tang *Zebrasoma flavescens*

Acanthurus flavescens Bennett, 1828. Hawaiian Is.

Hawaiian Islands, Micronesia and Ogasawara Islands. This species co-occurs with the closely related *Zebrasoma scopas* in Micronesia and southern Japan where they inter-breed. Although they are possibly sub-specific or even just geographical variants, the xanthic form is best served as a separate taxon. It occurs in shallow protected waters, forming large schools in Hawaii and Guam. Juveniles are usually solitary amongst corals. In southern Japan this species occurs in mixed groups with *Z. scopas* and the two species behave like they are one. These yellow individuals may actually be a xanthic form of *Z. scopas*. In the same area the xanthic juveniles of *Acanthurus pyroferus* are common and rare xanthic forms in other fishes, such as kyphosids, are a regular occurrence. Some brown individuals from Okinawa changed to yellow in the Toba Aquarium. Length to 20 cm.

B

Z. flavescens or xanthic Z. scopas. Iriomote I., Japan. D. 10 m. L. 10 cm.

C

Z. flavescens. Hawaii. Juvenile.

D

Z. flavescens. Hawaii. Adults.

E

Z. flavescens. Juvenile in aquarium.

Z. flavescens. Guam, Micronesia. Depth 15 m. Length 16 cm.

Z. flavescens. Hawaii. Schooling adults. Ed Robinson.

Yellow-tail Sailfin Tang
Zebrasoma xanthurum

Acanthurus xanthurus Blyth, 1825. Sri Lanka.

Red Sea and Arabian Sea, ranging to Sri Lanka. Doubtfully reported in the Maldives. Occurs on rubble reefs to about 20 m depth. Adults are usually either in pairs or schools. Small juveniles secretive amongst large corals. This species is readily identified by its bright colouration and shape. Length to 25 cm.

Z. xanthurum. Aquarium, Sri Lanka export. Length 15 cm.

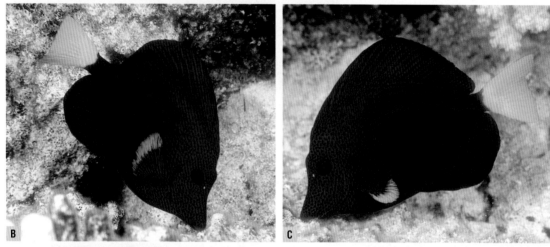

Z. xanthurum. **B-D** Egypt, Red Sea. Depth 20 m. Length about 20–22 cm.

Z. xanthurum. United Arabian Emirates. Depth 15 m. Length 20 cm.

Z. xanthurum. United Arabian Emirates. Depth 15 m. Schooling adults.

Acanthurus gemmatus
Valenciennes, 1835. Mauritius.

Indian Ocean, known from South Africa to Madagascar and Mauritius. Also known as Mauritius Tang. Usually seen on open reefs or swimming over mixed sand and rubble, adjacent to reefs to a moderate depth. Reported to 60 m, but usually occurs in much shallower waters. A territorial species that is nearly always found singly. Readily identified by the distinctive colouration of black with numerous white spots and a yellow tail. Length to 18 cm.

Z. gemmatum. Aquarium. Length 15 cm.

Z. gemmatum. Mauritius. Depth 20 m. **B** Length 12 cm. **C** Length 5 cm. Roger Steene.

Z. gemmatum. Mauritius. Depth 20 m. **D** Length 18 cm. **E** Length 8 cm.

Long-snout Sailfin Tang
Zebrasoma rostratum

Acanthurus rostratum Günther, 1875. Society I.

Only known from the south Pacific, Marquesas to Cook Islands, Tuvalu and Pitcairn. Occurs in lagoons and on protected reefs to about 15 m depth. Adults readily identified by their black colour and long snout. Very similar to *Zebrasoma scopas*, co-occurs and inter-breeds in some areas. **A** appears to be a hybrid. Length to 21 cm.

A
Z. rostratum? Tuvalu, S. Pacific. Kendall Clements.

B
Z. rostratum. Cook Islands, South Pacific. Depth 15 m. Length 20 cm.

C
Z. rostratum. Cook Islands, South Pacific. Depth 15 m. Length 20 cm.

SUBFAMILY **NASINAE – UNICORNFISHES**

The subfamily Nasinae is represented by the single genus *Naso* containing nearly 20 species. Unicornfishes have an ovate and elongate body (elongating more with age), tapering posteriorly to a very shallow caudal-peduncle, and the body is moderately compressed. They have a single long-based, very low dorsal fin of even height that originates above the end of the head. The caudal fin is truncate to very lunate, depending on age and species, and the pectoral fins are small and rounded to somewhat pointed. The mouth is small and placed about level with the body-axis, and contains numerous small teeth which are slender and sharp with serrated edges, numbering about 60–80 in each jaw. Eyes are placed high and laterally on the head. The peduncular spines develop with age into one or two large, forward-hooked spines, that are fixed on plates on each side of the caudal peduncle.

Most species form large schools as adults and feed on plankton along reef walls or in outer reef passages where currents carry lots of plankton during tidal flows. Juveniles are mainly seen grazing algae on the substrate, but most adults feed on algae as well as zooplankton and species that are usually seen in open water are at times observed grazing on the substrate. Most species grow large, over 50 cm, and are not suitable for the average home aquarium. However, some species are very attractive and a few aquarists have built large aquariums to house such beauties. Public aquariums with tropical displays normally have several species of *Naso* in the main aquariums on display, shared by sharks and large groupers that may prey on them, but these fishes seem to handle such a situation very well.

This is what a large home reef-aquarium can look like with a good selection of *Naso*, the rare siganid *Siganus uspi* and various other small fishes. The owner who took this photograph, Daniel Knop, is obviously a devoted aquarist and has a very impressive set-up with a harmonious environment to be proud of, with fish displaying excellent colour, indicating that water conditions are perfect. Surgeons and rabbitfishes are sensitive to conditions and go dark when unhappy.

Table. 2. Fin-formulas of species of Nasinae, Prionurinae, and related families.

	Dorsal fin		Anal fin		Pectoral fin	Ventral fin
Naso annulatus	V–VI	28–29	II	27–30	17–19	I, 3
Naso brachycentron	IV–V	29–30	II	27–28	17	I, 3
Naso brevirostris	V–VI	28–29	II	25–30	16–17	I, 3
Naso caeruleacaudus	IV	30	II	29	17	I, 3
Naso caesius	VI–VII	27–29	II	27–29	16–18	I, 3
Naso fageni	V	24–26	II	23–25	17	I, 3
Naso hexacanthus	VI	26–29	II	27–30	17–18	I, 3
Naso lituratus	VI–VII	27–30	II	28–30	15–17	I, 3
Naso elegans	VI	28–30	II	28–30	16–17	I, 3
Naso lopezi	V	28–31	II	27–29	17	I, 3
Naso maculatus	VI–VII	26–28	II	26–28	16–18	I, 3
Naso minor	V	27–29	II	27–30	16–17	I, 3
Naso thynnoides	IV	28–30	II	27–29	17–18	I, 3
Naso tonganus			II			I, 3
Naso tuberosus	V	27–29	II	26–27	16–18	I, 3
Naso unicornis	V–VI	27–30	II	27–29	17–18	I, 3
Naso vlamingii	VI	26–27	II	26–29	16–19	I, 3
Naso n. sp			II			I, 3
Prionurus biafraenis	VIII	25	III	21	15	I, 5
Prionurus laticlavius	VII–VIII	27–28	III–IV	23	18	I, 5
Prionurus maculatus	IX	24–26	III	23–25	17–18	I, 5
Prionurus microlepidotus	VIII	21–22	III	20–21	16	I, 5
Prionurus punctatus	VII–VIII	25–26	III	23		I, 5
Prionurus scalprus	IX	22–24	III–IV	21–23	16–18	I, 5
Prionurus sp						I, 5
Zanclus cornutus	VII	40–43	III	33–36	18–19	I, 5
Siganus spp	XIII	10	VII	9	15–19	I, 3, I
Luvarus imperialis adult	I	11–13	I	12–14	14–18	I
juvenile	I	21	I	16–18	17–20	I, 3–4
Scatophagus argus	X–XI	16–18	IV	14–15	17	I, 5
Selenotoca multifasciata	XII	16	IV	15–16	17	I, 5
Chaetodipterus faber	IX	21–23	III	18–19	17–18	I, 5
Chaetodipterus zonatus	IX	18–23	II–III	16–20	17–18	I, 5
Drepane longimana	VIII–IX	19–23	III	17–19	16–18	I, 5
Drepane punctata	VIII–IX	19–22	III	17–19	16–18	I, 5
Ephippus orbis	IX	19–20	III	15–16	15	I, 5
Parapsettus panamensis	IX	28	III	24	18	I, 5
Platax batavianus	VII	26–32	III	21–23	18–19	I, 5
Platax boersii	V	32–34	III	25–27	18–19	I, 5
Platax orbicularis	V	35–37	III	26–27	17–18	I, 5
Platax pinnatus	V–VI	34–37	III	25–27	17–19	I, 5
Platax teira	V	29–33	III	22–26	16–18	I, 5
Tripterodon orbis	IX	19-21	III	15–17	17–19	I, 5
Zabidius novemaculatus	IX	29	III	22	24	I, 5

Fig. 1. Selected features of *Naso*.

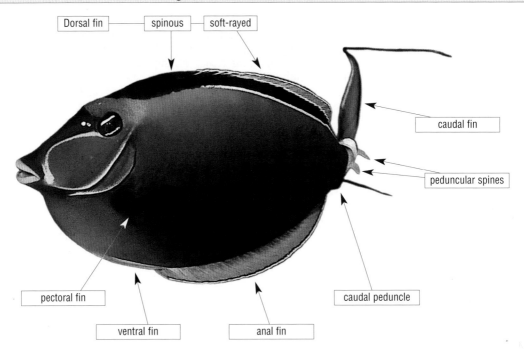

Dorsal fin — spinous — soft-rayed

caudal fin

peduncular spines

pectoral fin

caudal peduncle

ventral fin

anal fin

Characteristics of the genus *Naso*.
Body oblong and compressed, elongating with age; caudal peduncle very narrow, with 1 or 2 bony plates on the sides that bear keel-like spines, often recurving in large adults; dorsal fin spines IV–VII, first usually longest; anal fin spines II, an additional rudimentary one hidden under skin at base of first; ventral fin I, 3; caudal fin from slightly rounded to deeply emarginate, developing long filaments on the corners in some species and sometimes only in the male.

Naso brevirostris. G.B.R., Australia. Showing the horn in front of the eyes, a feature in several species, and the thin 'tuna-like' peduncle is typical for this genus. Caudal fin shapes vary greatly between the species from rounded to deeply emarginate. Phil Woodhead.

Masculine. Type species: *Naso fronticornis* Lacepéde, 1801 (synonym of *Naso unicornis*, Forsskål, 1775). A distinctive genus: oval-slender bodied with pointed snout, thin caudal peduncle, and adults of some species with horn-like projection on forehead. Comprises about 18 species that are variously distributed in the Indo-Pacific. The taxonomic status of some closely related species or geographical variations is under investigation and the exact number of species depends on the outcome. Most species are widespread, showing no significant differences over large geographical areas. Unlike most other surgeonfishes that feed primarily on algae or detritus in the shallows, the unicornfishes feed also on zooplankton and occur over a much larger depth range. Some species have been recorded several hundreds of metres down. Colour is highly variable in some of the species, and this often relates to behaviour. An individual can change colour quickly to adapt to the environment for camouflage, or may turn-on bright colours during displays, fights, courtship and spawning. During feeding in open water, the colour of most species is usually uniform with dark shading on top, paling to a much lighter colour below, as typically seen in pelagic fishes. When on the bottom of the ocean the colours usually change in various ways, depending on behaviour, and most dramatically during fights or courtship. Most species have diagnostic colour markings that are useful for identifying them, even as juveniles, such as a certain colour lips or peduncular spines. Sexual dimorphism in this group is reflected in males being larger, with much more developed spines on the peduncular plates. The horn-like projection on the forehead of some species is usually present in the adults of both sexes, but in a few it is a male-only feature. Certain species develop filaments on the caudal fin and in the males of some species these become extremely long.

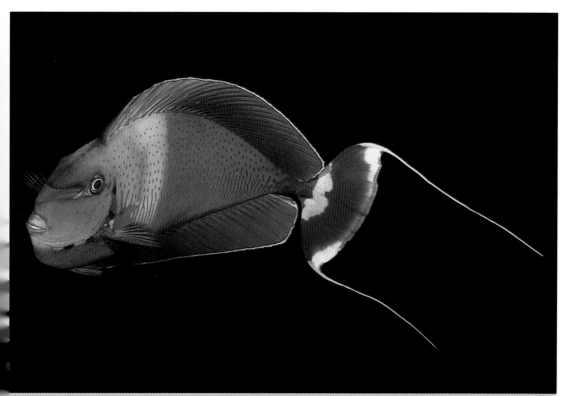

Naso vlamingii develops extremely long filaments on the tips of the caudal fin, which is thought to be a male-only feature. Unlike many other *Naso* males, this species develops no horn, but the forehead becomes strongly rounded and hump-like in large males, often extending well in front of the mouth. This colourful species is typically found in schools along reef walls and steep slopes and is one of the most widespread species in the Indo-West Pacific, showing no or only slight colour differences between distant geographical populations.

Behaviour

Adults typically form schools in open water along reefs, where some species feed on zooplankton. Juveniles feed primarily on benthic algae and gradually adapt from grazing to adult behaviour. Adults too, will feed on benthic algae at times to compliment their main diet of zooplankton. Unicornfishes can be quite colourful, but when feeding in open water, their principal colour serves as camouflage, being silvery on their sides, greenish on top and white below. When coming back to the reefs, to sleep, looking for a cleaner, or interacting with their own kind, various different colour patterns are employed by different species for different occasions. Visiting a cleanerfish usually results in the fish going very pale, while disputing males or those courting females can change colour dramatically with irridescent hues. They are capable of changing colour within seconds.

Tiny juveniles are rarely noticed by divers. They settle from their transparent prionurus stage when about 40-45 mm long and hide amongst rocks or rubble along reef edges. Once coloured, they start venturing out into the open and usually join other algae grazers that are similar in size as a form of protection in numbers. These can be a mix of related or unrelated species such as small sawtails or triggers. They are even seen feeding with juvenile butterflyfishes that form small groups when feeding on benthic invertebrates.

Naso annulatus. Great Barrier Reef, Australia. A typical school of adults along the outer reef wall. Phil Woodhead.

Naso lituratus. Hawaii. A school of adults milling above the sea bed. Ed Robinson.

lituratus 104

elegans 106

vlamingii 108

unicornis 110

brachycentron 112

annularis 114

brevirostris 116

tuberosus 118

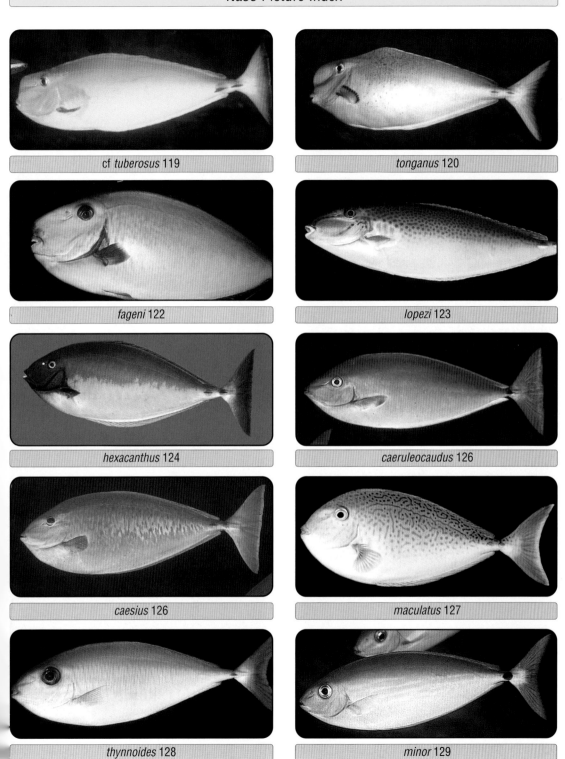

cf *tuberosus* 119

tonganus 120

fageni 122

lopezi 123

hexacanthus 124

caeruleocaudus 126

caesius 126

maculatus 127

thynnoides 128

minor 129

A

N. lituratus, Cook Islands, South Pacific. Depth 20 m. Length 45 cm.

Pacific Orange-spine Unicorn
Naso lituratus

Acanthurus lituratus. Forster, 1801. Tahiti.

Widespread West and central Pacific. Replaced by *Naso elegans* in the Indian Ocean and Red Sea. Coastal and inner reef flats and slopes. Adults usually in small groups or schools. Juveniles on shallow rocky reefs, sometimes in small aggregations mixed with other small acanthurids. Adults are identified by their orange double peduncular spines. Distinguished from *Naso elegans* by the broad black band along dorsal fin base and orange anal and ventral fins versus yellow dorsal and dusky ventral and anal fins. Both species can be found together in Bali. Length to 45 cm, excluding the caudal fin filaments.

B

N. lituratus, night. Bali, Indonesia. Depth 15 m. Length 40 cm.

C

N. lituratus. Sangihe I. Depth 5 m. Length 75 mm.

N. lituratus. Bali, Indonesia. Depth 5 m. Length 40 cm.

E   *N. lituratus*, Qld, Australia. Depth 7 m. Length 15 cm.

F   *N. lituratus*, Kerama, Japan. Depth 20 m. Length 15 cm.

G   *N. lituratus*. Sangihe I., Indonesia. Depth 5 m. Length 75 mm. Individual with very long caudal fin filaments, probably a male.

H   *N. lituratus*. Hawaii. Depth 20 m. Schooling adults, some of which are grazing algae on the seabed.

Indian Orange-spine Unicorn
Naso elegans

Apisurus elegans. Rüppell, 1829. Red Sea.

Widespread Indian Ocean and Red Sea, ranging to Bali, Indonesia. Occurs on coastal and sheltered reef flats in small groups and schools in oceanic locations such as the Maldives or Christmas Island. Identified by its orange peduncular spines and distinguished from its Pacific cousin by its yellow dorsal fin, and dusky to black ventral and anal fins. The two species were found together in Bali where *Naso lituratus* greatly out-numbers and dominates *N. elegans*, evident by the scar inflicted by that species shown in the photograph below. Length to 45 cm.

N. elegans. Night. Egypt, Red Sea. Length about 35 cm.

N. elegans. Egypt, Red Sea. Large adult with long caudal fin filaments, probably a male.

N. elegans. Bali, Indonesia. Depth 5 m. Length 40 cm. The scar was inflicted by *N. lituratus* that out-numbers this species here.

N. elegans. Juvenile in aquarium. Origin unknown.

N. elegans. Maldives. Depth 15 m. Length 40 cm.

N. elegans. Red Sea. **F** large male. **G** Schooling adults along reef edge.

Acanthurus vlamingii. Forster, 1801. Tahiti.

Widespread Indo-West Pacific, but some geographical variation. Found on clear coastal to outer reef habitats, forming loose schools along upper regions of deep drop-offs. Readily identified by its colour and in all stages, from juvenile to adults, the lips are blue and 'blue-lipped unicorn' would be a more appropriate name. Like most unicorns, it can change colour dramatically and quickly when coming from open water to visit reefs to sleep or when visiting cleaning stations, as shown in the photographs. Length to 55 cm. excluding filaments on caudal fin.

N. vlamingii. Cook Islands, South Pacific. Depth 16 m. Length 50 cm.

N. vlamingii, night. Flores, Indonesia. Depth 20 m. Length 45 cm.

N. vlamingii. Bali. D. 4 m. L. 5 cm. T. Tonozuka.

N. vlamingii. Kerama, Japan. Depth 20 m. Length 35 cm.

N. vlamingii. Bali, Indonesia. Depth 15 m. Length 25 cm.

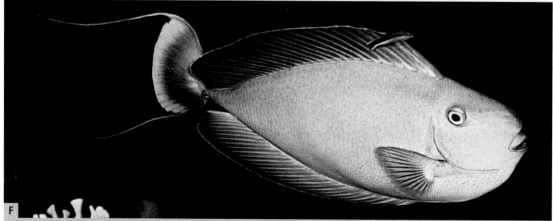

N. vlamingii. Bali, Indonesia. Depth 6 m. Length 45 cm. With changed colour to assist cleaner wrasse.

N. vlamingii. Bali, Indonesia. Depth 15 m. Length 55 cm. A long-tailed male.

N. vlamingii. Maldives. Depth 20 m. A diver observing anemone fishes is in turn being observed by these unicorns.

Blue-spine Unicorn *Naso unicornis*

Chaetodon unicornis. Forsskål, 1775.
Red Sea.

Widespread Indo-West Pacific. Various reef habitats, inshore, lagoons as well as deep waters along outer reef walls. Juveniles in shallow protected bays and harbours. Adults have a relatively short horn, usually not reaching past the mouth. Readily identified by the blue blotch surrounding each peduncular spine, which is also present during the juvenile stage. Length to 70 cm.

N. unicornis. Bali, Indonesia. Depth 15 m. Length 35 cm.

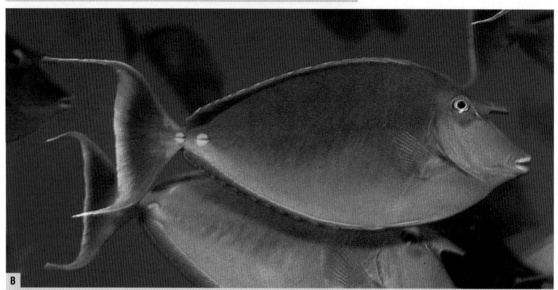

N. unicornis. Red Sea. Depth 20 m. Length 60 cm.

N. unicornis. Midway, Hawaiian Islands. Large adults, length about 60–65 cm. Kendall Clements.

N. unicornis. **D** juvenile, NSW, Australia. Depth 5 m. Length 5 cm. **E** nuptial male. Bali, Indonesia. Depth 25 m. Length 65 cm.

N. unicornis. Bali, Indonesia. Depth 25 m. Length 50 cm.

Humpback Unicorn
Naso brachycentron

Naseus brachycentron. Valenciennes, 1835. Waigeo.

Widespread Indo-West Pacific. Deep coastal to outer reef slopes usually in small groups but occasionally in large schools. Adults are identified by their humped back, and only males have the long horn in front of their eyes. Juveniles are plain grey and have a white peduncle. Length to 70 cm.

N. brachycentron. Night, Bali, Indonesia. Depth 15 m. Length 35 cm.

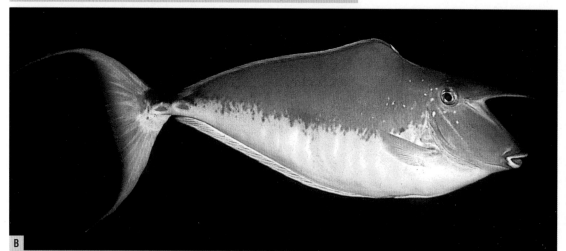

N. brachycentron, male. Maldives. Depth 20 m. Length 65 cm.

N. brachycentron, female. Maldives. Depth 20 m. Length 50 cm.

N. *brachycentron*. Male. Lakshadweep, India. Depth 20 m. Large male. (Hugues Vitry).

N. *brachycentron*. Bali, Indonesia. Depth 15 m. Schooling adults, mixed sex, length 50-65 cm. Takamasa Tonozuka.

Priodon annulatus.
Quoy & Gaimard, 1825. Timor.

Widespread Indo-West Pacific. Deep, clear coastal to outer reef slopes usually in small groups but occasionally in large schools. Adults are identified by their long horn and the white margin on the caudal fin. Juveniles are grey with white caudal peduncle. Largest unicorn, length to over 1 m, including the horn.

N. annulatus. **A** Qld, Australia. Large juvenile, length about 25 cm. **B** Sydney, NSW. Small juvenile, length 45 mm. Depth 4 m.

N. annulatus. Queensland, Australia. Length about 25 cm. Depth 4 m.

D

N. annulatus. Bali, Indonesia. Depth 20 m. Length 85 cm. Takamasa Tonozuka.

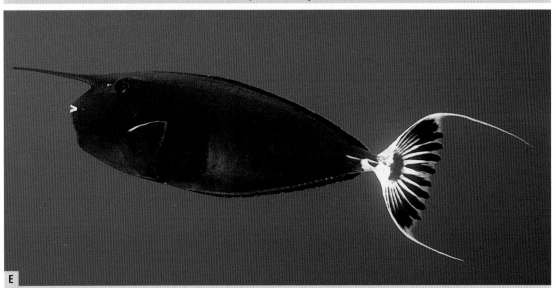

E

N. annulatus. Great Barrier Reef, Australia. Depth about 18 m. An incredible looking large male, length about 1 m. Kendall Clements.

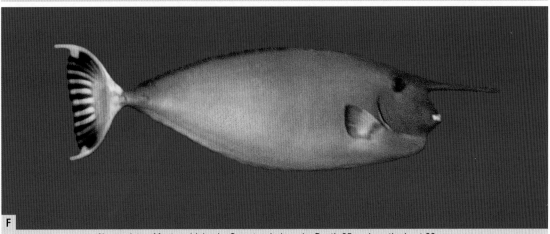

F

N. annulatus. Mentawai Islands, Sumatra, Indonesia. Depth 25 m. Length about 90 cm.

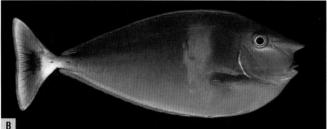

Spotted Unicorn *Naso brevirostris*

Naseus brevirostris. Cuvier, 1829. No locality.

Widespread Indo-West Pacific. Various coastal to outer reef habitats. Common species usually in small groups but form large schools in oceanic locations or along reefs subject to strong currents. Identified by a long horn even when fish is relatively small. Caudal fin bluish grey to white and body and head spotted, with spots forming lines in adults. Length to 50 cm.

N. brevirostris, female. Egypt, Red Sea. Depth 15 m. Length 45 cm.

N. brevirostris. **B** Female, developing horn. Solomon Islands. Neville Coleman. **C** Juveniles. GBR, Qld. Length 15 cm.

N. brevirostris, male. Mauritius. Depth 15 m. Length 45 cm.

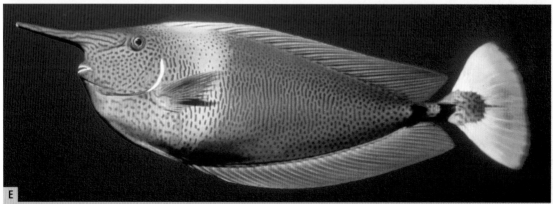

N. brevirostris, nuptial male. Red Sea. Depth 20 m. Length 50 cm.

N. brevirostris, schooling. Maldives. Length ~35 cm.

N. brevirostris, schooling. Bali, Indonesia. Depth 15 m. Length ~45 cm. Takamasa Tonozuka.

Black-spot Unicorn *Naso tuberosus*

Naseus tuberosus. Cuvier, 1829. No locality.

Distribution unknown, due to the wide use of the name for other species, but appears to be restricted to the western Indian Ocean. A rarely seen species that may have a preference for deep water. Identified by the shape of its head and markings, a black stripe in front of the eye and a large black spot in front and down from the pectoral fin base. Sub-adults have numerous tiny dark spots over their back, on the dorsal fin and caudal fin. Reaches at least 60 cm.

N. tuberosus, male. Mauritius. Depth 25 m. Length 60 cm. Hugues Vitry.

N. tuberosus, male. Mauritius. Depth 25 m. Length 60 cm. Hugues Vitry.

Square-nose Unicorn *Naso* cf *tuberosus*

Previously confused with *Naso tuberosus*.
Appears to be undescribed.

Widespread Indo-West Pacific. Coastal to outer reef, usually at moderate depth in reef channels subject to strong currents, or gathering around rocky outcrops along shores. Often occurs singly but sometimes forms small groups. A plain species in which the male develops a squarish-shaped hump on the snout. Length to 60 cm.

A

N. cf *tuberosus*, male. Maldives. Depth 20 m. Length 60 cm.

B

N. cf *tuberosus*, male. Maldives. Depth 20 m. Length 60 cm.

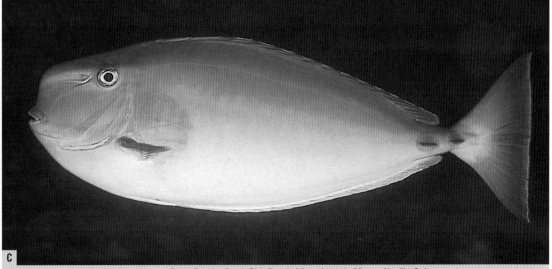

C

N. cf *tuberosus*. Great Barrier Reef, Qld. Depth 25 m. Length 50 cm. Neville Coleman.

Hump-nose Unicorn *Naso tonganus*

Naseus tonganus. Valenciennes, 1835.
Tongatabou.

Widespread Indo-West Pacific. Previously misidentified as *Naso tuberosus*. Adults usually seen on outer reef habitats, on crests near deep water or along steep walls, occurring singly or in small groups. Males develop a large hump in front of the eyes. Juveniles and females are plain greenish grey with numerous small dusky to yellow spots. Length to 60 cm.

N. tonganus. **A** female. Milne Bay, PNG. Depth 15 m. Length 35 cm. **A** juvenile. Sydney, Australia. Depth 4 m. Length 5 cm.

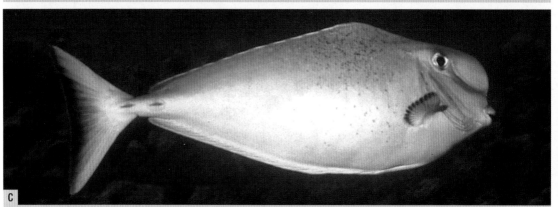

N. tonganus. GBR, Australia. Depth 15 m. Length 45 cm. Phil Woodhead.

N. tonganus, male. Coral Sea. Depth 8 m. Length 55 cm. Neville Coleman.

E   *N. tonganus*, Seychelles. Depth 25 m. Length 50 cm.

F   *N. tonganus*, in mixed school, including *Acanthurus lineatus*. Great Barrier Reef, Australia. Depth 7 m. Length 40–45 cm.

G   *N. tonganus*. Great Barrier Reef, Australia. Depth about 10 m. Length about 50 cm. Kendall Clements.

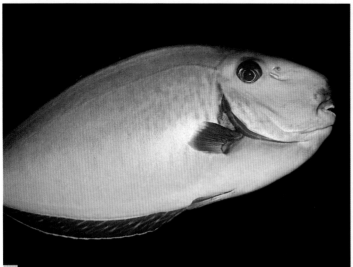

Horse-face Unicorn *Naso fageni*

Nasofageni. Morrow, 1954. Philippines.

Widespread Indo-West Pacific. Inner and outer reefs, usually schooling near reefs, feeding either on plankton in open water or on the seabed with rubble and algae substrates. Appears to be uncommon throughout its range and occasionally seen mixed with other large unicorn species. This species is rarely seen as shown in the picture below. Males develop a short and rounded horn just above the mouth. Length to 80 cm.

N. fageni. Nancy Aquarium, France. Length 40 cm.

N. fageni. Seychelles. Depth 25 m. Length 45–50 cm.

Slender Unicorn *Naso lopezi*

Naso lopezi. Herre, 1927. Philippines.

Widespread West Pacific. Coastal to outer reef slopes subject to strong currents. Sometimes in large schools. Adults are identified by their slender body shape and the numerous dusky spots on the upper half of the body. Length to 60 cm.

N. lopezi. Flores, Indonesia. Night, depth 10 m. Length 35 cm.

N. lopezi. **B** & **C** Sulawesi, Indonesia. Depth 20 m. Length 50 cm.

N. lopezi. Komodo, Indonesia. Depth 15 m. Length ~50 cm. Takamasa Tonozuka.

Prionodon hexacanthus. Bleeker, 1855.
Ambon.

Widespread Indo-West Pacific. Coastal to outer reef slopes at various depths in pursuit of plankton, usually in large schools. Adults are identified by their blue caudal fin and double peduncular spine. Juveniles are plain pale blue, grey, or greenish with blue caudal fin. Length to 50 cm.

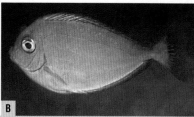

A

B

N. hexacanthus. **A** Flores, Indonesia. Depth 20 m. Length 45 cm. **B** Bali, Indonesia. Depth 15 m. Length 45 mm.

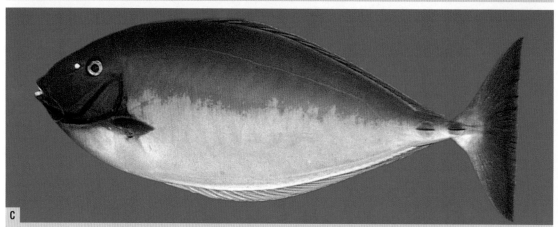

C

N. hexacanthus. Flores, Indonesia. Depth 10 m. Length 45 cm. Nuptial colour.

D

N. hexacanthus. Bali, Indonesia. Large adults, visiting a *Labroides* wrasses cleaning station.

E

N. hexacanthus. Bali, Indonesia. Depth 10 m. Length ~45 cm. Takamasa Tonozuka.

F

N. hexacanthus. Maldives. Sub-adults mixing with various reef fishes on the edge of a deep outer reef wall. Depth 7 m.

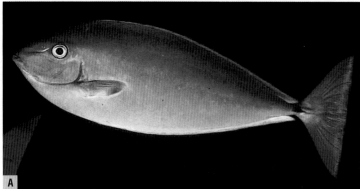

Naso caeruleacauda. Randall, 1994.
Philippines.

West Pacific, Philippines to Indonesia (east of Wallace's Line) and Coral Sea. Occurs in schools, mainly along outer reef walls and usually at moderate depths in pursuit of plankton. Underwater they are recognised by their overall blue colour and their shape. Closer examination reveals a single peduncular spine and a yellowish area on the body behind the pectoral fin. Length to 40 cm.

A

N. caeruleacaudus. Flores, Indonesia. Depth 25 m. Length 40 cm.

B

N. caeruleacaudus. Flores, Indonesia. Depth 20 m. Length 40 cm.

C

N. caeruleacaudus. Flores, Indonesia. Depth 20 m. Length 40 cm. Schooling along reef wall.

126

Silver-blotched Unicorn
Naso caesius

Naso caesius. Randall & Bell, 1992.
Marshall Islands.

Widespread Indo-West Pacific. Mainly occurs along upper edges of drop-offs on outer reefs in pursuit of plankton. Usually seen singly or in small groups, and often swims with schools of *Naso hexacanthus,* a similar species in shape and colour. Occasionally *N. caesius* turns on a pattern of silvery-grey blotches on its upper to middle sides. Length to 60 cm.

N. caesius. Timor Sea. Depth 20 m. Length 50 cm. Jerry Allen.

Scribbled Unicorn
Naso maculatus

Naso maculatus. Randall & Struhsaker, 1981. Hawaiian Islands.

Appears to be restricted to Pacific islands, ranging from Hawaii to Japan and the Coral Sea region south to Lord Howe Island. A deep water species that is rarely seen by divers in less than 20 m depth along steep reef walls, and the usual depth range reported is 40–100 m. Identified by the pattern of spots and scribbles over the upper sides, usually becoming finely spotted in large individuals. Length reported to 60 cm.

A

N. maculatus. Hawaiian Islands. Kendall Clements.

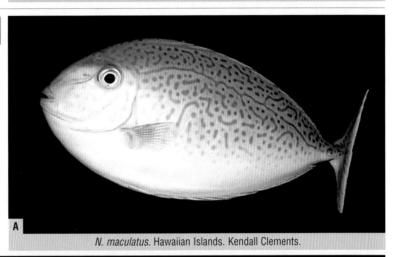

B

N. maculatus. Hawaiian Islands. Kendall Clements.

One-spine Unicorn *Naso thynnoides*

Axinurus thynnoides. Valenciennes, 1835.PNG.

Widespread Indo-West Pacific. Coastal to outer reef slopes, sometimes forming large schools. Usually seen swimming steadily along upper edges of drop-offs in pursuit of plankton. Identified by the yellowish area mid-laterally on the body, looking somewhat like a fusilier at distance. The single peduncular spine and fine vertical lines often present on the upper sides behind the head are only visible up close. Length to 35 cm.

N. thynnoides. Night colour. Bali, Indonesia. Depth 10 m. Length 30 cm.

N. thynnoides. Bali, Indonesia. Depth 10 m. Length 35 cm.

N. thynnoides. Iriomote I., Japan Depth 20 m. Length 30 cm.

N. thynnoides. Bali, Indonesia. Depth 10 m. Length 30 cm.

Little Unicorn *Naso minor*

Axinurus minor. Smith, 1966. Mozambique.

Widespread Indo-West Pacific. Coastal to outer reef slopes, usually swimming in small schools along upper edges of drop-offs. This species is rarely noticed, probably because of its small size. Identified by its black caudal peduncle with a single spine, and yellow caudal fin. Length to 30 cm.

N. minor. Flores, Indonesia. Depth 15 m. Length 30 cm.

N. minor. Flores, Indonesia. Depth 15 m. Length 30 cm.

SUBFAMILY **PRIONURINAE – SAWTAILS**

The subfamily Prionurinae is represented by the single genus *Prionurus* with members variously distributed in the Indo-Pacific and the Atlantic. Sawtail surgeons have a deep to ovate body (elongating with age), which is highly compressed and covered with numerous tiny scales, giving the skin a leathery appearance. The single dorsal fin is long-based and of even height, originating just above the end of the head. The anal fin is like a mirror image of the dorsal fin at the posterior end, originating about halfway between the snout and caudal fin base. The caudal fin is truncate to emarginate, depending on age and species, and the pectoral fins are of moderate size, the longest ray about equal to the length of the head, and pointed in shape. The mouth is small and placed just below the level of the body axis. The peduncular spines develop with age into three or seven sharp keels, that are fixed on plates on each side of the caudal peduncle.

Most species form large schools as adults and feed on benthic algae or in open water on suspended plant matter during tidal flows. Juveniles are mainly seen grazing algae on the substrate. The species grow to a moderately large size, about 40–50 cm, and are not suitable for the average home aquarium. In addition they have little appeal and are only occasionally seen in public aquariums.

Fig. 1. Selected features of *Prionurus*.

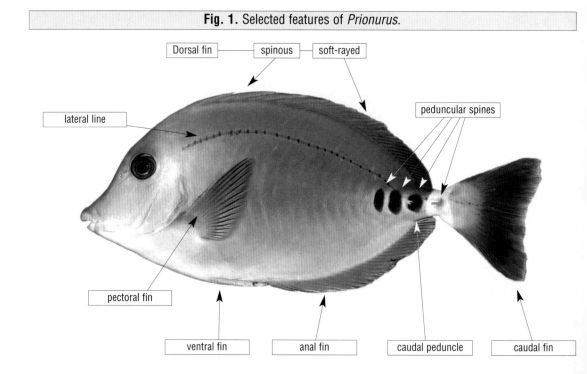

Characteristics of the genus *Prionurus*.
Body deep to oblong and compressed, elongating with age; lateral line distinct; caudal peduncle with series of bony plates on the sides that bear keel-like spines in adults; teeth incisor-like with denticulated edges, in single series of about 10 or more in each jaw; dorsal fin spines VII–IX; anal fin spines III–IV; ventral fin I, 5; caudal fin from truncate to emarginate.

Fin formulas of the species of the Prionurinae are presented in table 2 on page 97.

GENUS *Prionurus* Lacepéde, 1804

Masculine. Type species: *Prionurus microlepidotus* Lacepéde, 1804. There are 7 species known from tropical to sub-tropical seas of the Pacific and Atlantic, one of which was recently discovered in Indonesia and is undescribed. The species in this group are much more localised than the members of the other two acanthurid sub-families. Whilst they have basically the same larval stages as members of the other groups, settling on the substrate at about the same size and after a similar pelagic duration, the fact that they are more localised may be related to their apparent preference for cooler waters and certain habitat requirements. The sawtails are readily distinguished from other surgeonfishes by the series of bony plates on their caudal peduncle that number three or more in a row and usually have a very distinct lateral line. Colour is diagnostic for all the species and usually there are slight differences between the sexes. Colour may change with mood, at night or during courtship and spawning. Adults form schools where they are common, whilst juveniles are usually seen in small groups.

Prionurus Picture Index

microlepidotus 132

scalprus 133

maculatus 134

laticlavius 136

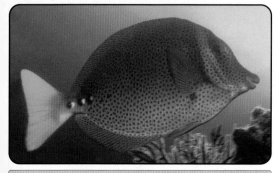

punctatus 137

biafraenis 138

Australian Sawtail
Prionurus microlepidotus

Prionurus microlepidotus. Lacepéde, 1804. NSW.

Eastern Australia from southern Queensland to southern NSW, including Lord Howe Island. A sub-tropical species that ranges into the tropical region of Queensland. Occurs in rocky estuaries as well as in coastal outcrops and islands off-shore. Juveniles are found in protected bays, usually in small groups grazing algae from rocks. Adults may form large schools in bays and around rocky outcrops along the shore. Identified by their long series of peduncular plates, numbering up to 7, uniform body colour and caudal peduncle which is white in adults and yellow in juveniles. Length to 50 cm.

P. microlepidotus. NSW, Australia. Depth 25 m. Length 25 cm.

P. microlepidotus. NSW, Australia. **B** night. Depth 8 m. Length 10 cm. **C** juvenile, 65 mm.

P. microlepidotus, male. NSW, Australia. Depth 10 m. Length 45 cm.

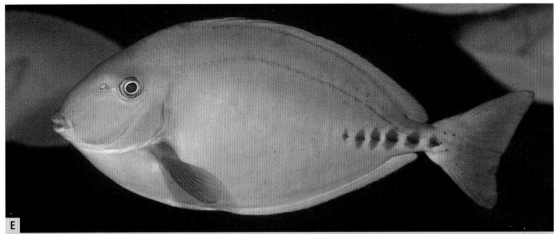

P. microlepidotus, large female. NSW, Australia. Depth 6 m. Length 40 cm.

P. microlepidotus, male. Southern GBR, Queensland. Depth 7 m. Length 50 cm. Neville Coleman.

P. microlepidotus, schooling. Southern GBR, Queensland. Depth 7 m. Length 45–50 cm. Neville Coleman.

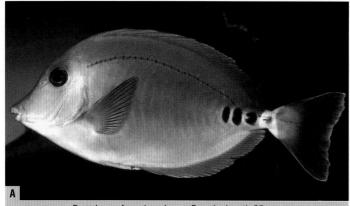

Japanese Sawtail
Prionurus scalprus

Prionurus scalprus. Valenciennes, 1835. Japan.

Sub-tropical Japan to Taiwan. Coastal bays in rocky-algal habitats where they usually occur in small groups. This is the only sawtail found in the region and is readily identified by its 4 or 5 bony peduncular plates of which 3 to 4 are black and bear feeble triangular keels. Juveniles and females are deep-bodied and have plain grey to nearly black body colouration. Males are much more elongate and are whitish ventrally with various, intermittent white streaks on the head and body. Length to 40 cm.

A

P. scalprus. Aquarium Japan. Female, length 25 cm.

B

P. scalprus. Aquarium Japan. Male, length 40 cm.

Spotted Sawtail
Prionurus maculatus

Prionurus maculatus.
Ogilby, 1887. Sydney, NSW.

Eastern Australia from southern Queensland to central NSW, including the Lord Howe Island region, and northern New Zealand. Occurs along coastal outcrops and islands off-shore, occasionally entering clear rocky estuaries. Juveniles are found in protected coastal bays, usually in small groups grazing algae from rocks. Adults may form large schools in bays and around rocky outcrops along the shore, feeding on benthic and floating algae in turbulent high energy zones in shallow water. Identified by the usually 3 blue peduncular plates, the yellow-spotted or barred pattern on the body, and blue fin margins. Length to 50 cm.

A

P. maculatus. Sydney Harbour, Australia. Sub-adult, length 30 cm.

B   *P. maculatus*. Lord Howe Island. Juvenile, 20 cm. Neville Coleman.

C   *P. maculatus*. Sydney, Australia. Night, length 10 cm.

D   *P. maculatus*. Lord Howe Island, NSW. Length about 40 cm. Neville Coleman.

E   *P. maculatus*. Solitary Islands, off NSW, Australia. Large adult, about 50 cm.

Galapagos Sawtail
Prionurus laticlavius

Naseus laticlavius.
Valenciennes, 1846. Galápagos.

Only known from the eastern Pacific, ranging from the Galapagos region to Panama. This species is the most common surgeonfish in the Galapagos where it is locally known as "chancho" or Yellow-Tailed Surgeonfish and swims in large dense schools in the shallows to about 15 m depth. Small juveniles form their own schools and are mainly yellow. Length to 30 cm.

P. laticlavius. Cocos I., eastern Pacific. Length 30 cm. Herwarth Voigtmann.

P. laticlavius. Cocos Island, Costa Rica, eastern Pacific. Length 25–30 cm. Herwarth Voigtmann.

P. laticlavius. Galapagos, eastern Pacific. Length 25–30 cm.

Californian Sawtail
Prionurus punctatus

Prionurus punctatus. Gill, 1862. California.

East Pacific, known from Gulf of California to El Salvador. Occurs in the shallows on rocky shores to about 20 m depth, usually forming large schools as adults. This species is almost identical to *Prionurus laticlavius* but has numerous dark spots over the head and body. Small juveniles are similar to adults and are sometimes all yellow. Length to about 35 cm.

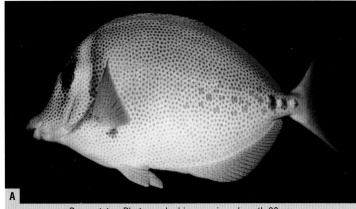

A

P. punctatus. Photographed in aquarium. Length 30 cm.

B

P. punctatus. Sea of Cortez, Mexico. Depth 15 m. Length 35 cm.

C

P. punctatus. Sea of Cortez, Mexico. Depth 15 m. Length 35 cm.

Atlantic Sawtail
Prionurus biafraenis

Xesurus biafraenis.
Blanche & Rossignoi, 1961. Sao Tomé.

Only known from the eastern Atlantic from the Gulf of Guinea to Congo. Occurs around shallow rocky reefs to about 10 m depth. *Prionurus biafraenis* is the only Atlantic member in the genus and the closest relatives are in the eastern Pacific. Readily distinguished from other surgeonfishes in the region by having a series of fixed plates with keels on the caudal peduncle, instead of the single, scalpel-like and movable spine. Length to 30 cm.

P. biafraenis. São Tomé, eastern Atlantic. Depth 10 m. Length 30 cm. Peter Wirtz.

Indonesian Sawtail
Prionurus sp

Undescribed species.

Only known from southern Indonesia, Indian Ocean parts of Bali to western Flores. Swim in loose groups around rocky outcrops, usually in high energy zones. This is the only sawtail known from the region and appears to prefer areas with cool up-wellings. Easily identifed by its colouration and the presence of peduncular plates. Length to 30 cm.

P. sp. Bali, Indonesia. Depth 3 m. Length 25 cm.

This family is represented by a single genus and species - see general section below.

Masculine. Type species: *Chaetodon cornutus* Linnaeus, 1758. There is only one species of Moorish Idol and it is widespread in the tropical Indo-Pacific, ranging well into sub-tropical zones with pelagic stages transported by currents. Pelagic larvae can travel great distances and may reach a large size, with post larvae usually measuring about 8 cm in length. The juvenile stage was described as *Chaetodon canescens* and the adult stage as *C. cornutus* in the same publication, and both names are in use by recent authors. The validity of either name was never resolved, but at present, most authors use *Zanclus cornutus*. Considering the vast geographical range, this species shows no variation, suggesting a good gene-flow between the populations that may relate to the long oceanic pelagic stage. The ancestral fossil *Eozanclus* suggests that this species evolved from the acanthurids a long time ago, retaining its distinctive form.

The moorish idol has a reputation for being difficult to keep in captivity. However, some individuals have lived for many years in aquariums. Juveniles adapt more easily to captivity than adults and their diet of mixed algae and invertebrates, such as sponges, may be difficult to substitute with other foods or to maintain a correct balance to keep the fish healthy.

Characteristics of the genus *Zanclus*.
Body very deep and compressed; third dorsal fin spine extremely long, usually much longer than the body; snout pointed and elongated in adults, mouth small with slender, and slightly incurved small teeth in jaws.

Fin formula: D VII, 40–43; A III, 33–36; P. 18–19; V I,5.

Z. cornutus. Lembeh Strait, Sulawesi, Indonesia. Adults schooling and feeding from a rock substrate.

Moorish Idol
Zanclus cornutus

Chaetodon cornutus. Linnaeus, 1758.
Indian Seas.

Widespread Indo-Pacific, East Africa to Central America. Various coastal to outer reef habitats. Commonly seen in pairs, occasionally forming large travelling schools. Readily identified by its colour and shape. Length to 16 cm.

Z. cornutus. Bali, Indonesia. The distinctive head features up close.

Z. cornutus, juveniles. **B** Guam, Micronesia. **C** Sydney, Australia. Post larval, 8 cm. **D** Flores, Indonesia. Length 10 cm.

Z. cornutus. **E** Bali, Indonesia. Pairing adults. Length 16 cm. **F** Cook Islands, South Pacific. Juveniles, 10 cm.

G *Z. cornutus.* Mauritius. A pair of adults, as they are most often seen. Length about 16 cm.

H *Z. cornutus.* Flores, Indonesia. Adults travelling in a school through a large inner reef lagoon.

I *Z. cornutus.* Palau, West Pacific. Adults travelling in a large school along the outer reef. Ed Robinson.

FAMILY **SIGANIDAE – RABBITFISHES**

A tropical Indo-Pacific family with a single genus and about 30 species. Two sub-genera: *Lo* and *Siganus* of which in *Lo* the snout is much more pronounced. They are also distinguishable as two groups by habitat: reef species, that are generally colourful and readily identified by colour, and seagrass species, that are all very similar and very difficult to tell apart, even from specimens. All the similar species have near identical morphology, the same meristics and, in the seagrass species, there are only slight colour-pattern differences. Spots may be round, elongated, few or many, but sometimes the patterns are useful to separate them as species. Rabbitfishes have an unusually high number of spines in their fins, 7 spines in the anal fin (most reef fishes have 3 or less) and a spine at both end of the ventral fins (most reef fishes have one anteriorly only), and all spines are venomous. A stab causes agonising pain. They feed primarily on weeds and algae grazed from rubble, coral bases and seagrasses. Reef species are often in pairs, and sometimes in schools, whilst most seagrass species are usually found in schools. They grow to about 30–45 cm in length.

Fig. 1. Selected features of *Siganus.*

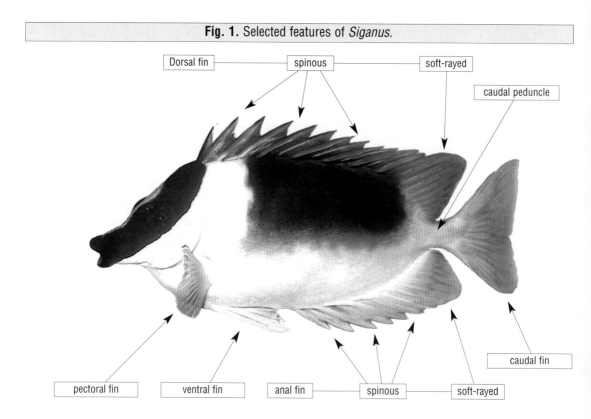

Dorsal fin — spinous — soft-rayed — caudal peduncle — pectoral fin — ventral fin — anal fin — spinous — soft-rayed — caudal fin

Characteristics of the genus *Siganus*.
Body deep to oblong and strongly compressed, elongating with age, covered with minute cycloid scales; mouth small, terminal and jaws with a row of slender incisor-like teeth which are slightly serrated, bi- or tricuspid ; dorsal fin rays XIII, 10, a spine projecting forward from first, usually buried under the skin; anal fin rays VII, 9; ventral fin I, 3, I; caudal fin from truncate to emarginate. All fin spines are venomous, with the glands at their bases.

Fin formulas between species of Siganidae are the same, except for some slight differences in the pectoral fin count.

GENUS *Siganus* Lacepéde, 1804

Masculine. Type species: *Siganus rivulatus* Forsskål, 1775. There are at least 30 species variously distributed   throughout the Indo-West Pacific and species from the Red Sea have migrated via the Suez canal to the Mediterranean Sea. It seems likely that more species will be recognised amongst the similar species associated with seagrasses. The distribution of most species is limited to certain regions and there are a number of sibling species between Indian and Pacific oceans, and other regions. Their pelagic stage is relatively short and reaches a size of about 20–25 mm   maximum and some post larvae caught in seagrasses were as small as about 15 mm total length. Spawning behaviour varies between the species, some pair and others form large schools that relate to tides and the lunar cycle.

The colourful members of the subgenus *Lo* are sought after for the aquarium and are relatively easy to keep. Requirements are similar to species of surgeonfish. Handling any of the species should be done with care as a stab from the fin spines is extremely painful. In Australia the fishermen refer to these fishes as 'happy moments', since stab victims on trawlers are usually seen dancing on the deck!

Siganus as food.

Tiny juvenile siganids, neatly stacked in jars with preservatives, on offer for sale on the Okinawa fish market in Japan.

Most of the species that use seagrass beds as nursery grounds are harvested in great numbers, at all available sizes. They are regarded as good food in many parts of south-east Asian waters and various other parts of the Indo-Pacific region, including the Red Sea, Arabian Gulfs and even in the eastern Mediterranean where they have only recently arrived. Rabbitfishes can make up a large proportion of the local fish available and are an important food source in many countries. They are also of economic importance and attract high prices at local fish markets, particularly those species that are considered to taste good as adults.

Various species have been studied for their potential in marine aquaculture. Their fecundity is apparently high, producing one quarter to half a million eggs per spawning season. The larval stage is approximately 3–4 weeks and their food comprises phytoplankton and zooplankton. They are sexually mature in one year and the larger species reach maximum size in a few years.

Siganus Picture Index

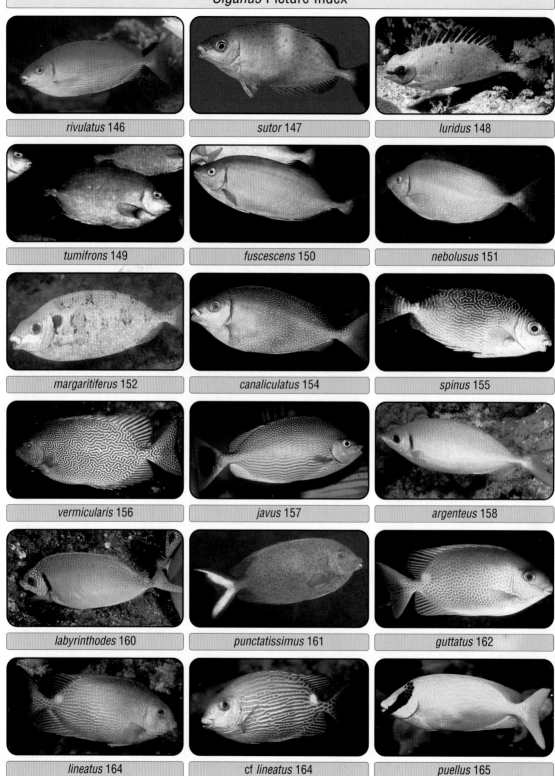

rivulatus 146	*sutor* 147	*luridus* 148
tumifrons 149	*fuscescens* 150	*nebolusus* 151
margaritiferus 152	*canaliculatus* 154	*spinus* 155
vermicularis 156	*javus* 157	*argenteus* 158
labyrinthodes 160	*punctatissimus* 161	*guttatus* 162
lineatus 164	cf *lineatus* 164	*puellus* 165

Siganus Picture Index

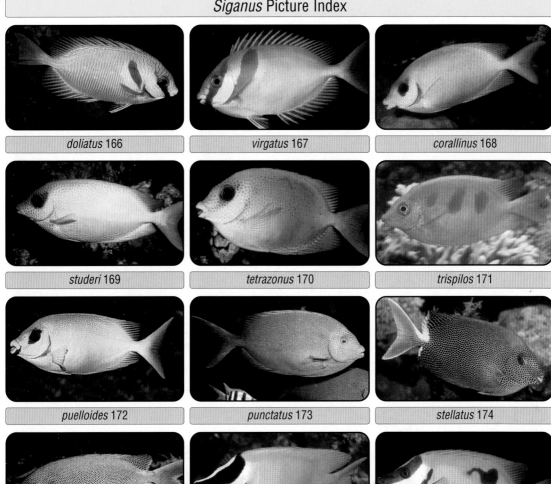

| doliatus 166 | virgatus 167 | corallinus 168 |

| studeri 169 | tetrazonus 170 | trispilos 171 |

| puelloides 172 | punctatus 173 | stellatus 174 |

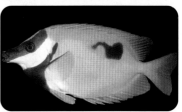

| laqueus 175 | vulpinus 176 | unimaculatus 177 |

| uspi 178 | magnificus 179 |

Red Sea Rabbitfish
Siganus rivulatus

Siganus rivulatus. Forsskål, 1775. Red Sea.

Red Sea and western Indian Ocean. It has spread to the eastern Mediterranean through the Suez canal and is now common and of commercial value there. This species forms small to moderate schools in sheltered bays around reefs with sand and algae substrates. It is best identified by the brownish, wavy lines running along the lower sides. Usual length to about 40 cm, but reported larger in some areas, especially the Arabian Gulf.

S. rivulatus. Egypt, Red Sea. Depth 3 m. Length 30 cm.

S. rivulatus. Egypt, Red Sea. Depth 3 m. Length 30 cm.

S. rivulatus. Seychelles. Depth 5 m. Length 30 cm.

African White-spotted Rabbitfish *Siganus sutor*

Amphacanthus rivulatus. Valenciennes, 1835. Seychelles.

Restricted to the western Indian Ocean, South Africa to Kenya, Seychelles and Madagascar regions. Occurs in shallow weedy habitats of estuaries and sheltered bays, usually marginally on rocky and coral reefs. Adults form large schools where common. Juveniles often in seagrass beds where they form small schools and graze algae from the seagrass leaves. Colour variable with mood, but regularly with pale, bluish-white spots on the body, some about pupil-sized and often with dark centres when adult. At night, or when caught, it usually has a distinct dark 'ear' blotch and white spots. A large species that can reach 50 cm.

A

S. sutor. Mauritius. Depth 2 m. Length 20 cm. Jerry Allen.

B

S. sutor. Sodwana Bay, South Africa. Depth 8 m. Length 35 cm. Kendall Clements.

C

S. sutor. Sodwana Bay, South Africa. Depth 10 m. Length 45 cm. Kendall Clements.

147

A

S. luridus. Red Sea. Length 25 cm. Jerry Allen.

B

S. luridus. Egypt, Red Sea. Depth 3 m. Length 30 cm.

C

S. luridus. Oman, Arabian Sea. Night. Length 20 cm. Phil Woodhead.

Dusky Rabbitfish *Siganus luridus*

Amphacanthus luridus. Rüppell, 1829. Red Sea.

Western Indian Ocean, Arabian Sea, Red Sea, and has become established in the eastern Mediterranean since migrating through the Suez Canal. Occurs on shallow algae reefs, coral reef flats, or rubble substrates, usually at depths of less than 10 m. Adults occur singly or in small groups. Small juveniles are often in rock pools and may form immense schools in protected bays. Identified by their truncate caudal fin, plain brown to green coloured body and occasional dark band in front of the eyes. A small species, length to about 25 cm.

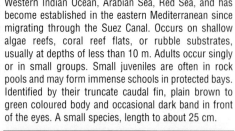

D

S. luridus. Red Sea. Massing juveniles.

E

S. luridus. Greece, Mediterranean. Depth 3 m. Length 25 cm. Peter Wirtz.

Amphacanthus tumifrons. Valenciennes, 1835. Shark Bay, Western Australia.

Western Australia, Shark Bay to the Kimberleys and islands off the coast. Sometimes travel in enormous schools over algal reefs. Juveniles occur in seagrasses and on algae reef-flats. This species is dusky brown to greenish with a few pale spots on its sides. It is deeper bodied compared to other similar species in the area and the caudal fin is distinctly truncate to slightly rounded. Length to 35 cm.

A

B

S. tumifrons. **A** juvenile. Jerry Allen. **B** Ningaloo Reef, Western Australia. Depth 10 m. Length 35 cm.

C

S. tumifrons. Ningaloo Reef, Western Australia. Depth 10 m. Length 35 cm.

Japanese Rabbitfish *Siganus fuscescens*

Centrogaster fuscescens. Houttuyn, 1782. Japan.

Appears to be restricted to subtropical waters of Japan, southward from the Iwate Prefecture. Replaced by other species in the more tropical Ryukyu Islands. Range uncertain due to erroneous use of name for several other species as far as Australia. Adults form large schools around rocky coastal outcrops. Juveniles in sheltered bays and probably in seagrass beds. Colour variable from green-brown to bright gold with bluish spots. Juveniles pale green and may have a more blotched pattern, depending on surroundings. Length to 30 cm.

S. fuscescens. Aquarium, Japan. Length 20 cm.

S. fuscescens. Aquarium, Japan. Length 25 cm.

S. fuscescens. Aquarium, Japan. Length 30 cm.

Happy Moments *Siganus nebulosus*

Amphacanthus nebulosus.
Quoy & Gaimard, 1825. Sydney, Australia.

Eastern Australia, ranging from southern NSW to Queensland. A schooling species in estuaries and harbours, usually on silty reefs and in seagrass habitats. Juveniles settle in seagrass beds after larval stage. Adults are deeper bodied than the more tropical *Siganus margaritiferus* that overlaps in range in southern Queensland. *S. nebulosus* has numerous pearly spots over its sides, about 1/2 pupil-size, and sometimes shows a black 'ear' mark. Length to 30 cm.

A

S. nebulosus. Sydney, Australia. Length 20 cm.

B

S. nebulosus. Southern NSW, Australia. Length 20 mm.

C

S. nebulosus. Sydney, Australia. Length 10 cm.

D

S. nebulosus. Southern NSW, Australia. Length 30 mm.

E

S. nebulosus. Sydney, Australia. Length 20 cm.

F

S. nebulosus. Central NSW, Australia. Length 25 cm.

Pearly-Spotted Rabbitfish
Siganus margaritiferus

Amphacanthus margaritiferus.
Valenciennes, 1835. Ambon.

Widespread Indo-West Pacific, ranging from southern Japan to Australia, and west to Andaman Sea. May involve several species. In-shore, algae reefs, estuaries and harbours. Juveniles in seagrasses when small. Adults usually in pairs on algae reefs, but sometimes seen schooling in oceanic locations. Adults are identified by the numerous small, white and mostly round spots on the body, a yellowish area over the head, and a dusky edge on the gill-plate. Sometimes dark spots are scattered over the body and there is sometimes an 'ear' blotch, that can fade in and out quickly. Small juveniles are yellow to green and usually occur in seagrass habitats. Length to 25 cm.

S. margaritiferus. Bali, Indonesia. Depth 8 m. Length 25 cm.

S. margaritiferus. Qld, Australia. D. 4 m. L. 25 cm.

S. margaritiferus. Qld, Australia. D. 4 m. L. 25 cm. Neville Coleman.

S. margaritiferus, juveniles. **D** Bali, Indonesia. D. 5 m. L. 35 mm. Takamasa Tonozuka. **E** Flores, Indonesia. D. 2 m. L. 65 mm.

S. margaritiferus. Flores, Indonesia. Depth 4 m. Length 10 cm. Dark spots on the body are intermittent.

S. margaritiferus. Bali, Indonesia. Depth 8 m. Length 25 cm. This large individual has small white spots.

153

White-Spotted Rabbitfish
Siganus canaliculatus

Chaetodon canaliculatus. Park, 1797. Sumatra.

Widespread Indo-West Pacific, and ranging west to southern India. Adults and juveniles in-shore, mangroves, algae reefs, estuaries and in large lagoons with algae-rubble habitats. Mainly common on rocky substrates. Usually seen singly or in small groups at shallow depths. Identified by its greyish, dusky body with numerous white spots, which elongate horizontally with growth. Length to 30 cm.

A S. canaliculatus. Bali, Indonesia. Depth 6 m. Length 30 cm.

C S. canaliculatus. Java, Indonesia. D. 3 m. L. 10 cm.

B S. canaliculatus. Mentawai I., Sumatra. Depth 3 m. Length 12 cm.

D S. canaliculatus. Night, Java, Indonesia. L. 10 cm.

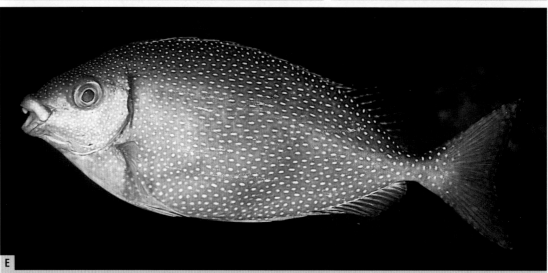

E S. canaliculatus. Bali, Indonesia. Depth 6 m. Length 30 cm. Typical adult pattern of spots.

Scribbled Rabbitfish *Siganus spinus*

Sparus spinus. Linnaeus, 1758. Java.

Widespread West Pacific, ranging to Andaman Sea and to the central Pacific. Shallow coastal and inner reef flats with rich algae growth. Adults usually occur in small groups, whilst juveniles gather in larger numbers in corals with algae growth at their bases. Easily identified by the pattern of lines on the body and barring on the caudal fin base. Length to 20 cm.

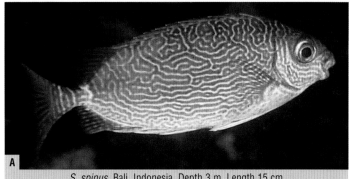

A

S. spinus. Bali, Indonesia. Depth 3 m. Length 15 cm.

B

S. spinus. Flores, Indonesia. Depth 5 m. Length 35–40 mm.

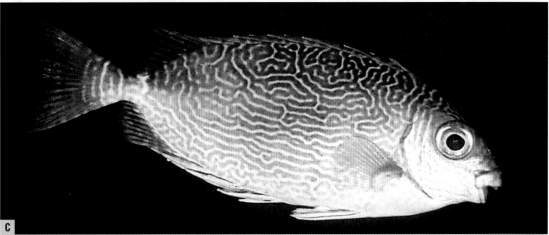

C

S. spinus. Bali, Indonesia. Depth 3 m. Length 20 cm.

Maze Rabbitfish *Siganus vermiculatus*

Amphacanthus vermiculatus.
Valenciennes, 1835. New Guinea.

Widespread Indo-West Pacific, ranging west to India. Adults on deep coastal reefs subject to strong currents. Both adults and juveniles school. Juveniles up to a moderate size often in estuaries. Identified by the maze-like pattern on the body and spotted caudal fin. Colour variable from pale greenish grey to brown, the head and body with darker to black scribbly lines or spots. Spots usually confined to head, but sometimes extend over most of the body and median fins. Length to 35 cm.

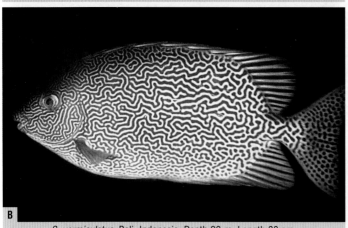

S. vermiculatus. Bali, Indonesia. Depth 20 m. Length 30 cm.

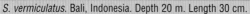

S. vermiculatus. Bali, Indonesia. Depth 20 m. Length 30 cm.

S. vermiculatus. As **D**.

S. vermiculatus. Lembeh Strait, Sulawesi, Indonesia. Depth 15 m. Length 30–35 cm.

Java Rabbitfish *Siganus javus*

Theuthis javus. Linnaeus, 1766. Java.

Widespread West Pacific and northern Indian Ocean to the Arabian Sea, into the Arabian Gulf. Coastal reefs and large estuaries. Usually seen in small groups but occasionally schooling in large numbers. Readily identified by the pattern of white spots and lines on the body and the large black blotch centrally on the caudal fin. Length to 40 cm.

A

S. javus. Java, Indonesia. Depth 3 m. Length 35 cm.

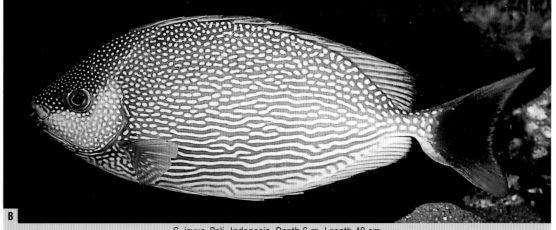

B

S. javus. Bali, Indonesia. Depth 6 m. Length 40 cm.

C

S. javus. Sri Lanka. Depth 8 m. Length 30–45 cm. Feeding on sea-jelly.

Schooling Rabbitfish
Siganus argenteus

Amphacanthus argenteus.
Quoy & Gaimard, 1825.
Guam and Mariana Islands.

Widespread Indo-West Pacific. Coastal and inner reefs, along slopes and in lagoons. Usually occur in large schools that swim fast and well above the substrate, occasionally all diving down to the bottom to feed. Identified by its slender body, colouration, and behaviour. Caudal fin is normally deeply forked, but some populations have a strongly lunate fin and some authors have suggested the possibility that this form represents another species. Both forms are known from Japan and the Maldives. Length to 30 cm.

S. argenteus. Flores, Indonesia. Depth 8 m. Length 20 cm.

S. argenteus. Iriomote I., Japan. Depth 20 m. Length 30 cm.

S. argenteus. Great Barrier Reef, Australia. Depth 15 m. Length 30 cm.

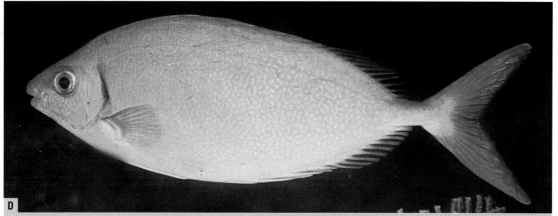

S. argenteus. Bali, Indonesia. Depth 6 m. Length 30 cm.

S. argenteus. Flores, Indonesia. Depth 8 m. Length 24 cm. Adults travelling along reef wall.

S. argenteus. Seychelles. Depth 8 m. Schooling adults.

Labyrinth Rabbitfish
Siganus labyrinthodes

Amphacanthus labyrinthodes.
Bleeker, 1853. Java.

Only known from Java and Bali with doubtful reports from Andaman Sea and Philippines. Occur in pairs on shallow coastal reefs. Identified by the almost all yellow and blue irregular scribbling over the head and body. Caudal fin lunate. Length to 25 cm.

S. labyrinthodes. Bali, Indonesia. Depth 6 m. Length 24 cm. Takamasa Tonozuka.

Fine-Spotted Rabbitfish
Siganus punctatissimus

Siganus punctatissimus.
Fowler & Bean, 1929. Philippines.

Widespread West Pacific. Coastal reefs, often near steep slopes, and harbours. Adults usually in pairs. An elusive species and, although common, is rarely noticed. It looks dark, greenish black, when seen at a distance with pale yellow streaks in the caudal fin that identifies the species. The body is covered with tiny dark spots that are recognisable only when up very close. Length to 35 cm.

S. punctatissimus. Lembeh Strait, Sulawesi, Indonesia. Depth 5 m. Length 25 cm.

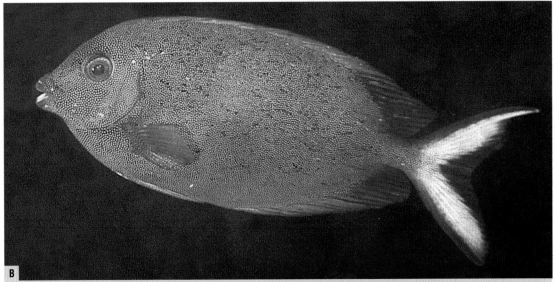

S. punctatissimus. Solomon Islands. Depth 15 m. Length 30 cm. Neville Coleman.

S. punctatissimus. **C** Bali, Indonesia. D. 8 m. L. 35 cm. Takamasa Tonozuka. **D** GBR, Australia. D. 20 m. L. 35 cm.

A

S. guttatus. Bali, Indonesia. Depth 8 m. Length 40 cm.

Gold-saddle Rabbitfish
Siganus guttatus

Chaetodon guttatus.
Bloch, 1787. East Indies.

Widespread West Pacific. Coastal to inner reef slopes. Adults are usually seen in small aggregations along reefs near caves or below large overhangs, but occasionally form large schools. Small juveniles in estuaries and amongst mangroves. Identified by the large golden saddle-spot below the end of the dorsal fin and its densely spotted body. Length to 40 cm.

B

S. guttatus. Similan I., Andaman Sea. Depth 8 m. Length 30 cm. Mark Strickland.

C

S. guttatus. Sumatra. L. 45 mm.

D

S. guttatus. Flores, Indonesia. L. 10 cm.

E

S. guttatus. Bali, Indonesia. Depth 6 m. Length 35–40 cm.

S. guttatus. Bali, Indonesia. Depth 6 m. Length 35 cm.

S. guttatus. Sipadan, Borneo. Depth 10 m. Length 35–40 cm. Ed Robinson.

Lined Rabbitfish
Siganus lineatus

Amphacanthus lineatus.
Valenciennes, 1835. Waigeo.

Widespread in the eastern part of the western Pacific and replaced in Indonesia by the closely related *Siganus guttatus,* south and west from Molluccen seas. Occurs on inner reefs, usually found in small groups near reef overhangs. Identified by the golden round saddle mark on the caudal peduncle and the numerous golden lines on the head and body. Length to 35 cm.

A

S. lineatus. GBR, Australia. Depth 15 m. Length 35 cm.

B

S. lineatus. GBR, Australia. Depth 15 m. Length 35 cm.

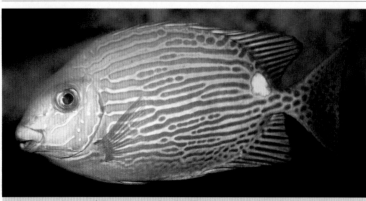

Siganus cf. *lineatus.* Sri Lanka. Depth 10 m. L. 25 cm. Roger Steene.

Sri Lankan Rabbitfish
Siganus cf *lineatus*

Undescribed species.

Only known from Sri Lanka, southern India, the Laccadive archipelago and northern Maldives atolls. Replaced by the closely related *Siganus guttatus* from the eastern Andaman Sea to the West Pacific. Occurs in coastal waters and on sheltered reefs, singly or in small groups. Length to at least 25 cm, probably to 35 cm.

Masked Rabbitfish *Siganus puellus*

Amphacanthus puellus.
Schlegel, 1852. Ternate I, Moluccas.

Widespread West Pacific. Clear coastal and sheltered inner reefs, usually in coral and other invertebrate-rich areas to about 10 m deep, occasionally deeper. Identified by its combined colour and slender shape and single black band which runs from over the eye to the chin, continued above the eye as spots. Length to 30 cm.

A

S. puellus. Bali, Indonesia. Depth 10 m. Length 30 cm.

B

S. puellus. Flores, Indonesia. Length 10 cm.

C

S. puellus. Flores, Indonesia. Length 16 cm.

D

S. puellus. GBR, Australia. Depth 20 m. Length 25 cm. Phil Woodhead.

E

S. puellus. Flores, Indonesia. Depth 8 m. Length 25 cm.

Siganus doliatus. Cuvier, 1830. Buru I.

West Pacific, replacing the closely related *Siganus virgatus* east of Sulawesi, ranging into the Pacific and eastern Australia. Occurs on clear coastal reefs, adults nearly always in pairs or occasionally in small groups. Identified by the distinctive pattern of irridescent blue lines on the yellow to orange body. Length to 25 cm.

A

S. doliatus. Solomon Islands. Depth 10 m. Length 25 cm. Neville Coleman.

B

C

S. doliatus. Juveniles. Bitung, Sulawesi, Indonesia. Depth 12 m. Length 10 cm.

D

S. doliatus. Pairing adults. Great Barrier Reef, Australia. Depth 12 m. Length 25 cm.

Double-bar Rabbitfish *Siganus virgatus*

Amphacanthus virgatus. Valenciennes, 1835. Java.

West Pacific and eastern Indian Ocean from Western Australia to India, mainly west of Wallace's line and in southern Indonesia east to Flores. Adults pair on coastal reef flats, slopes, and in estuaries. Small juveniles in mangroves and in freshwater, moving to reefs where usually in small groups amongst corals. Length to 24 cm.

A

S. virgatus. Java, Indonesia. Depth 3 m. Length 10 cm.

B

S. virgatus. Flores, Indonesia. Freshwater stream. Depth 1 m. Length 20 mm.

C

S. virgatus. Western Australia. D. 12 m. L. 24 cm. Neville Coleman.

D

S. virgatus. Java, Indonesia. Depth 3 m. Length 55 mm.

E

S. virgatus. Kerama, Japan. Depth 20 m. Length 20 cm.

F

S. virgatus. Bali, Indonesia. Depth 6 m. Length 20 cm.

G

S. virgatus. Andaman Sea. D. 10 m. L. 22 cm. Mark Strickland.

Indian Coral Rabbitfish
Siganus corallinus

Siganus corallinus.
Valenciennes, 1835. Seychelles.

Widespread Indian Ocean, ranging to Java. Coastal and inner invertebrate-rich reefs to about 10 m depth. Adults pair. Small juveniles on algae reef, forming small groups. Adult *Siganus corallinus* have a black patch under the mouth that distinguishes it from similar West Pacific species. Small juveniles are plain yellow. Length to 35 cm.

S. corallinus. **A** Maldives. Depth 8 m. Length 35 cm. Adult pair. **B** Java. Juvenile, about 40 mm, swimming with *S. virgatus*.

S. corallinus. Seychelles. Depth 4 m. Length 15 cm.

S. corallinus. Maldives. Depth 10 m. Length 35 cm.

Pacific Coral Rabbitfish
Siganus studeri

Teuthis studeri. Peters, 1877. New Britain.

West Pacific, ranging from eastern Australia and adjacent Pacific region to Irian Jaya. Clear coastal reefs and inner lagoons in rich coral and invertebrate habitats. Adults usually in pairs, swimming about openly over coral formations. Juveniles occur singly or in small numbers in *acropora* thickets. Adults identified by their bright yellow colour and numerous small blue ocelli on the head and body, and a black triangular patch on the eye. Small juveniles have a few blue spots on the head. Length to 30 cm.

S. studeri. Solomon Islands. Length 25 cm. Neville Coleman.

S. studeri. GBR. Australia. **B** Depth 8 m. Length 15 cm. **C** Length 10 cm. Phil Woodhead.

S. studeri. Great Barrier Reef, Australia. Depth 6 m. Length 24 cm. Phil Woodhead.

A
S. tetrazonus. Bali, Indonesia. Depth 30 m. Length 25 cm.

Indonesian Coral Rabbitfish
Siganus tetrazonus

Amphacanthus tetrazona.
Bleeker, 1855. Manado, Sulawesi.

West Pacific, ranging from southern Indonesia to Philippines. Coastal and inner reefs, usually in rich coral habitats. Adults occur solitary or in pairs. Small juveniles on coastal reefs at a moderate depth, usually at about 20 m or more. Mainly all orange-yellow with blue bars when very small and blue spots on the head when adult. Faint dusky barring on head, occasionally distinct through the eye, continuing over the snout, and along edge of gill-plate. Large adults with indistinct pale band between eye and gill-margin to behind the mouth. Length to 30 cm.

B
S. tetrazonus. Flores, Indonesia. Depth 7 m. Length 20 cm.

D
S. tetrazonus. Flores, Indonesia. L. 55 mm.

C
S. tetrazonus. Bitung, Sulawesi, Indonesia. D. 9 m. L. 14 cm.

E
S. tetrazonus. Bali, Indonesia. L. 75 mm.

F
S. tetrazonus. Bali, Indonesia. Depth 15 m. Length 25 cm.

Three-spot Rabbitfish
Siganus trispilos

Siganus trispilos. Woodland & Allen, 1977. Off North West Cape, Western Australia..

Known only from the north-western coast of Australia. Occurs on rich coral reefs to about 10 m depth. Adults usually seen in pairs. The highly visible dark blotches on the sides of *Siganus trispilos* readily identifies the species underwater, even at a long distance. Similar dark blotches are present in large juveniles and the night colour pattern of *S. tetrazona* suggests a close relationship. Length to 24 cm.

A

S. trispilos. Ningaloo Reef, Western Australia. Depth 7 m. Length 15 cm.

B

S. trispilos. Ningaloo Reef, Western Australia. Depth 10 m. Length 24 cm.

Siganus puelloides.
Randall & Woodland, 1979. Maldives.

Indian Ocean, Maldives and Seychelles to Andaman Sea. Occurs around clear-water rock and coral reefs with a mix of rich invertebrate and algae growth. Adults usually swim in pairs. *Siganus puelloides* is distinguished from the similar co-occurring *S. corallinus,* in having a more elongated body and a black marking under and behind the mouth that extends upwards to the upper lip. Length to 25 cm.

S. puelloides. Maldives. Depth 8 m. Length 25 cm. Roger Steene.

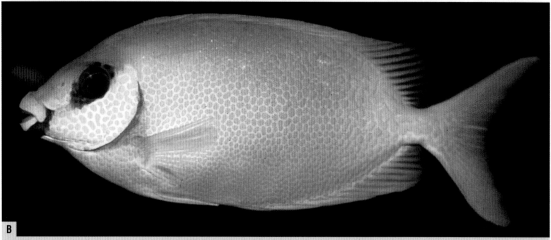

S. puelloides. Seychelles. Depth 10 m. Length 25 cm.

S. puelloides. Maldives. Depth 8 m. Length 25 cm. Adult pair. Jerry Allen.

Spotted Rabbitfish
Siganus punctatus

Amphacanthus punctatus.
Schneider, 1801. Tonga.

Widespread West-Central Pacific, ranging to west Sumatra. Adults occur mainly on deep coastal reefs, and juveniles usually in shallow estuaries. A deep bodied species, identified by the numerous small orange spots all over. Juveniles with less, but proportionally larger spots with interspaces in a mosaic pattern. Sometimes displays a dusky round 'ear' spot that is usually distinct at night. Length to 40 cm.

A *S. punctatus.* GBR, Australia. Depth 20 m. Length 40 cm.

B *S. punctatus.* Flores, Indonesia. D. 4 m. L. 55 mm.

C *S. punctatus.* Java, Indonesia. D. 4 m. L. 65 mm.

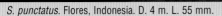

D *S. punctatus.* Bali, Indonesia. Depth 25 m. Length 35 cm.

Yellow-tail Starry Rabbitfish
Siganus stellatus

Scarus stellatus. Forsskål, 1775. Red Sea.

Endemic to the Red Sea. Replaced by *Siganus laqueus* in the Indian Ocean. Adults typically swim in pairs along reef margins to about 10 m depth. Readily identified by its bluish grey body with numerous black spots that cover most of the head and body, yellow-green over the back from behind the head and a large caudal fin that is mostly yellow, with this yellow colour often extending to the ends of the dorsal and anal fins. A deep-bodied species, reaching about 40 cm in length.

S. stellatus. Red Sea. Depth 8 m. Length 40 cm.

S. stellatus. Egypt, Red Sea. Depth 6 m. Length 35 cm.

S. stellatus. Egypt, Red Sea. Depth 6 m. Length 40 cm.

Grey-tail Starry Rabbitfish
Siganus laqueus

Siganus laqueus. von Bondé, 1934. Zanzibar.

Widespread Indian Ocean, ranging east along the south-western coast of Sumatra to Java. Occurs on algae-rich reefs, often in exposed surge zones or channels subject to very strong currents. Numerous pairs were seen in Sunda Strait but impossible to photograph due to raging currents. Usually in depths less than 10 m, but in the Maldives they were seen much deeper on a rubble seabed along the base of reefs. Identified by its grey colour and numerous black spots over the head, body and tail. Length to 40 cm.

Note: regarded as sub-specific from *Siganus stellatus* by recent ichthyologists, based on similarity in morphology. However, colour differs greatly between the two species, and there are also differences in the shape and proportional sizes of the fins, especially the caudal fin.

A

S. laqueus. Maldives. Depth 15 m. Length 25 & 35 cm.

B

S. laqueus. Maldives. Depth 15 m. Length 35 cm.

C

S. laqueus. Seychelles. Depth 15 m. Length 40 cm. Neville Coleman.

Fox-face
Siganus (Lo) vulpinus

Amphacanthus vulpinus.
Schlegel & Müller, 1845.
Ternate I, Moluccas.

Widespread Indonesia to Philippines and to central Pacific and eastern Australia. Replaced further north by *Siganus unimaculatus* and in Western Australia by another species very similar to *S. unimaculatus*. The fox-face occurs on sheltered rich coral and invertebrate reefs to about 15 m depth. Adults typically occur in pairs and juveniles may form small groups amongst corals. This species is easily identified by its bright yellow body and black and white head. Length to 25 cm.

S. vulpinus. Bali, Indonesia. Depth 8 m. Length 18 cm.

S. vulpinus. Flores, Indonesia. Depth 5 m. Length 10 cm.

S. vulpinus. Singapore. Depth 5 m. Length 30 mm.

S. vulpinus. Sangihe Islands, Indonesia. Depth 9 m. Length 23 & 25 cm.

Black-blotch Fox-face
Siganus (Lo) unimaculatus

Lo unimaculatus.
Evermann & Seale, 1907.
Luzon. Philippines.

Known from southern Japan to eastern Philippines. Occurs on rich coral reef slopes, often seen schooling over *Acropora* fields. Adults move about openly when in large schools and may swim long distances to feed. Where less common, they form pairs that stay near the seabed and are more wary. Juveniles hide amongst coral branches. Readily identified by their bright yellow-orange colour and black and white head. Normally with a distinctive large black blotch on sides, but this is highly variable in size and shape, from being absent to very large or double. Often abnormalities are on one side only. Length to 25 cm.

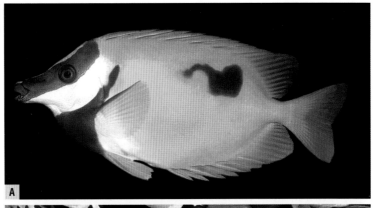

A

B

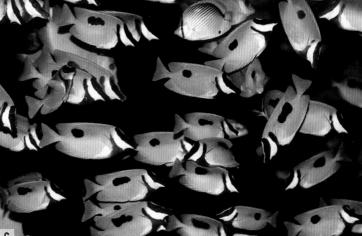

C

D

S. unimaculatus. Toba Aquarium, Japan. **B** juvenile, all others are adults, showing the great variability in the black side spot.

Black Fox-face
Siganus (Lo) uspi

Siganus uspi. Gawel & Woodland, 1907. Fiji.

Primarily known from the Fiji region and a few reported sightings from New Caledonia. The almost identical *Siganus (Lo) niger* from neighbouring Tonga differs in having a black tail and was described from two specimens only. Adults of both *S. uspi* and *S. niger* live in identical habitats, and are usually found in pairs along edges of shallow drop-offs and in deep depressions on reef crests where they feed on fleshy algae. They are readily identified by their nearly black colour and yellow pectoral fins. Only *S. uspi* has a yellow tail. Length to 24 cm.

S. uspi. **A** & **B** Fiji. Length about 24 cm. Kendall Clements.

S. uspi. Large juveniles. Aquarium. Daniel Knop.

S. uspi. Adult. Nancy Aquarium, France.

Andaman Fox-face
Siganus (Lo) magnificus

Lo magnificus. Burgess, 1977.
Phuket region, Thailand.

Known from the Andaman Sea to south-western Java. Fairly common in the Similan Islands where adults occur in pairs on coral reefs, ranging to a depth of at least 25 m. Juveniles are secretive in *Acropora* coral thickets, either singly or in small groups. A beautifully coloured species unlikely to be confused with any other rabbitfish. Length to 24 cm.

A

S. magnificus. Andaman Sea. Adult. Mark Strickland.

B

S. magnificus. Singapore Underwater World, public aquarium. Specimen from Sumatra. Length 22 cm.

C

D

S. magnificus. Mentawai I, off Sumatra, Indonesia. **C** Juvenile, length 8 cm. D. Pairing adults, about 24 cm long.

RELATED FAMILIES OF SURGEON AND RABBITFISHES

There are a number of families that belong in the acanthuroid group that are either little known or have only recently been included. The giant surgeonfish, *Luvaris imperalis,* Luvaridae - monotypic, lives in very deep water and is not included here. The largest family is Ephippidae, known as batfishes in the Indo-Pacific and spadefishes in the Americas. The various forms are sometimes placed in subfamilies. The two sicklefishes included with Ephippidae differ the most from the others in this family and are sometimes placed in their own family Drepanidae. Also recently included with the acanthuroids are Scatophagidae, the scats, with just two members.

FAMILY **EPHIPPIDAE – BATFISHES & SPADEFISHES**

The family Ephippidae is represented by 7 genera. The Indo-Pacific genus *Platax* is the largest with 5 species, *Chaetodipterus* and *Drepane* comprise 2 species and the rest, *Ephippus, Parapsettus* and *Zabidius* are monotypic. The various species are known as batfishes and spadefishes, relating to their shape. In general the body is almost circular with the rest of the profile made up by the shape of the fins. In some juveniles the dorsal and anal fins are extremely tall and deep, like wings, which proportionally decrease in size with age, with most adults becoming more 'spade' shaped, like the Atlantic species. Small juveniles are often very attractive and may be on offer in the aquarium fish trade. Unfortunately they grow quickly and to a large size, and most people will not be able to accomodate the adult fish. However, they make great pets and if space is not a problem they are highly recommended. Juvenile *Platax* have interesting early stages. The tiny juveniles mimic floating leaves, or crinoids, with one even mimicking a nasty tasting flatworm. Adults travel through open water in tight schools taking on shapes that, from a distance, look like large sea-creatures. One such school seen from a distance in clear water off an outer reef wall was mistaken for a sunfish.

PICTURE INDEX TO EPHIPPIID GENERA

Platax 181

Zabidius 200

Chaetodipterus 201

Parapsettus 202

Tripterodon 203

Ephippus 203

Drepane 204

Masculine. Type species: *Chaetodon teira* Bloch & Schneider, 1801 (= *Chaetodon teira* Forsskål, 1775). Comprises 5 species that are variously distributed in the Indo-West Pacific. Geographical distribution and the extent of their range differs between species and relates to their early stages. Widespread species have long pelagic larval and juvenile stages, some juveniles may drift with oceanic weed-rafts over great distances, whilst those much more localised in their distribution settle early as juveniles on the substrate. The members of the genus *Platax* are commonly known as 'batfishes', and its juveniles have long wing-like dorsal and anal fins that seem out of proportion with their small coin-like bodies. The sea-bats (Family Ognocephalidae) were wrongly listed as 'batfishes' amongst trawled species. Small juvenile *Platax* are solitary and juveniles of all these species have interesting behaviour with regards to camouflage and mimicry in their early stages. During development, some juveniles remain solitary whilst others may form small schools in sheltered parts of reefs. Large adults occur singly, in pairs or form massive schools. This variability in behaviour probably relates to the season, feeding, migration or spawning. Their diet is highly variable and includes algae and a large range of benthic or pelagic invertebrates.

Juvenile batfishes are popular aquarium fishes, but they are quick-growing and attain a large maximum side that may become a problem in a small aquarium. Whilst the juveniles are often extremely attractive with interesting colours and shape, the adults become rather dull and lose their long fins. However, they become very tame and make great pets.

Characteristics of the genus *Platax*.
Body almost circular in young, slightly elongated in adults, and highly compressed, mostly covered with finely ctenoid or cycloid scales, extending onto the fins; mouth small, terminal, and jaws with bands of small tricuspid teeth; dorsal fin spines V–VII (usually V), first short and the rest progressively longer, and soft rays numerous, ranging from 29–39, variable by 5 rays with some species; anal fin with III spines, with up to 29 soft rays; pectoral fin very small, with 16–19 rays; ventral fin I, 5 and extremely long in small juveniles; caudal fin from slightly rounded in juveniles to double emarginate in adults.

Fin formulas of *Platax* species are presented in table 2, page 97.

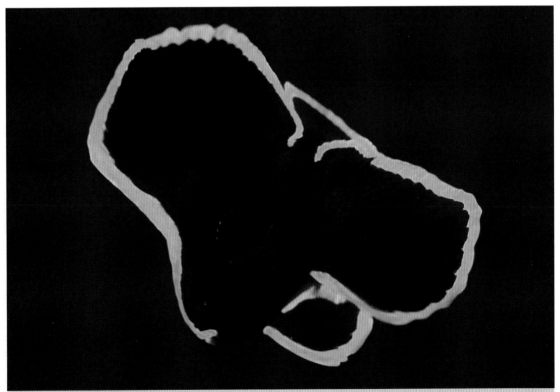

A tiny juvenile *Platax pinnatus*, just 25 mm long but 80 mm tall, is a 'fatal' attraction to an aquarist if for sale in a shop, but apparently this species is not as easily maintained as other batfishes. Photo: Takamasa Tonozuka.

Fig. 1. Selected features of *Platax*.

Dorsal fin — spinous — soft-rayed

lateral line

caudal fin

caudal peduncle

pectoral fin

ventral fin

anal fin

Juvenile behaviour

Little is known about Batfishes until they start their juvenile stage. Large adults are often seen in deep lagoons or along deep outer reef walls and the seemingly resident reef fish are either by themselves or in small groups. Yet, the same species may form enormous schools at times. One could speculate that this is for spawning purposes or for migration to other territories. Observations of spawning *Platax* have not been documented. What is known is that they produce numerous tiny eggs and hatched larvae are as small as 2.2 mm, whilst the largest collected larvae measured 18.5 mm long. The smallest juveniles, fully pigmented, are about the size of the largest larval fish. Juveniles of different species have adapted in different ways, all of which are very interesting. Several species are semi-pelagic, which means taking refuge with floating debris, and usually staying well away from the shore. When eventually drifting into coastal waters, small juveniles of *Platax teira* remain with floating debris and eventually adapt to a more benthic lifestyle, usually when finding companions of their own kind. Living near the surface in open water (see opposite page) has many dangers and juveniles form schools below weeds or employ other techniques to avoid predation. Juvenile *Platax orbicularis*, mimic floating debris such as leaves, which are plentiful just after the wet season. Juveniles of *Platax pinnatus* flatten themselves against the seabed and look convincingly like nasty tasting flatworms, whilst the juvenile of *P. batavianus* is well camouflaged when it stays near crinoids. Larger juveniles of *P. teira* and *P. orbicularis* are usually seen in small groups, but the other species seem to prefer a solitary life. The juveniles of *P. boersii* are least known because of confusion with other species. They may resemble either *P. teira* or *P. orbicularis*. However, moderately large juveniles of *P. boersii* are more distinctive and have been observed in pairs or in small aggregations.

The surface - 'the safest place'. **A** & **B** juvenile *Platax teira* start their lives on the surface, usually floating with loose weeds, especially the large *Sargassum* rafts after the wet season, dispersing this species over large areas. To photograph this stage, it is best to dive off-shore, as shown in **A** in the Flores Sea, Indonesia with the seabed several thousands of metres below. Photo: Roger Steene. **B** one of the results, showing a reflexion in the surface of the water. **C** a 35 mm juvenile *Platax orbicularis* flattens itself against the surface when approached, doing a magnificent job of mimicking a floating leaf. This photo was taken in coastal waters off eastern Sulawesi, Indonesia.

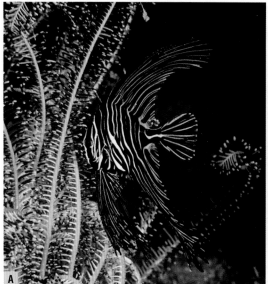

Platax batavianus, or the Zebra Batfish, knows the safest place is close to the sticky tentacles of crinoids. It has the ideal colour pattern <u>not</u> to be noticed. Like all *Platax*, they grow quickly and the beautiful zebra pattern is soon left behind. Large adults are more silvery and travel over open substrates. **A** Milne Bay, Papua New Guinea. Length about 40 mm. Depth 16 m. **B** Bali, Indonesia by Takamasa Tonozuka. Depth 30 m.

Platax boersii. Adults are known for their schooling behaviour along deep outer reef walls, and for their yellow appearance (see next page). These large individuals display a banded pattern, perhaps more suitable on the reef itself. This form is usually confused with *P. teira.* Photo: Flores, Indonesia, Depth 10 m. Length 20 mm. Alison Kuiter.

A

Platax boersii, schooling adults. This species has a yellow appearance, even at 40 m depth or more. The schools may comprise hundreds, perhaps thousands of individuals, often swimming so closely together that from a distance the school appears to be a single-bodied creature. Bali. Indonesia. Takamasa Tonozuka.

B

Platax orbicularis, schooling adults. This species is rarely seen in such large aggregations, especially on outer reefs such as here in the Banda Sea. This behaviour is likely to be for spawning purposes. Adults are usually seen in small aggregations in coastal waters or large lagoons.

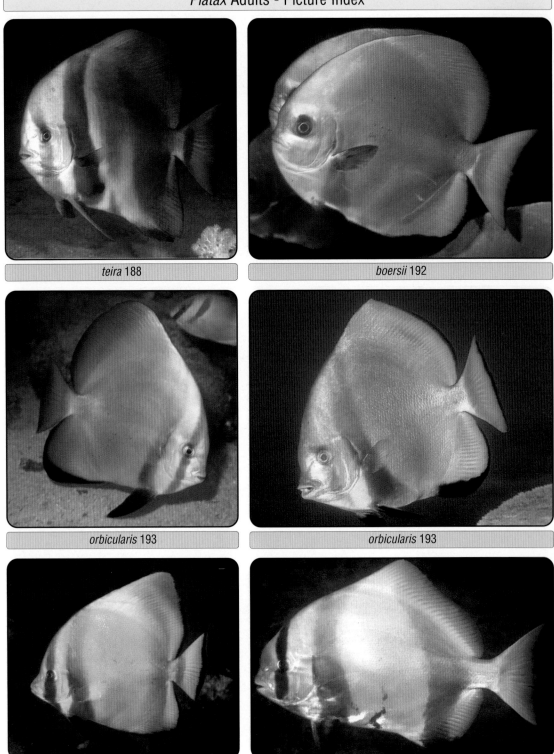

teira 188

boersii 192

orbicularis 193

orbicularis 193

pinnatus 194

batavianus 195

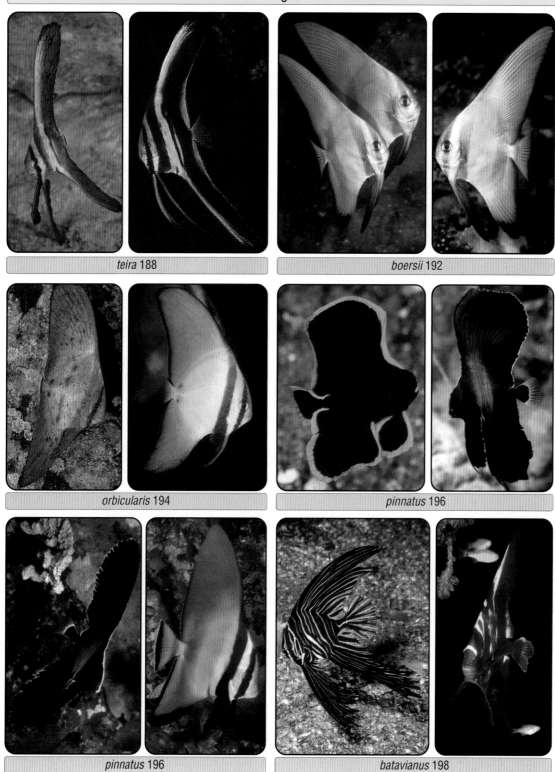

teira 188

boersii 192

orbicularis 194

pinnatus 196

pinnatus 196

batavianus 198

Tall-fin Batfish
Platax teira

Chaetodon teira. Forsskål. 1775. Red Sea.

Widespread Indo-West Pacific. The most common batfish seen by divers. Large adults occur in sheltered bays as well as deep off-shore. Often found around shipwrecks in small groups and occasionally form large schools. Small juveniles are found amongst floating debris and form aggregations as they find each other. They can be pelagic up to a large size and form schools under large *Sargassum* rafts that usually form after the wet season. Small juveniles are readily identified by their shape and colour. The tall-fin look remains up to a large size and adults have a diagnostic black blotch posteriorly at the lower end of the dark band behind the head. This blotch is less obvious when the band is dark and in sub-adults it only occurs as an irregularity in the shape of the band. Length to 45 cm, reported to 60 cm.

Easily kept and fast growing, but requires a large home.

P. teira. Queensland, Australia. Depth 20 m. Length 45 cm.

P. teira. Kerama, Japan. Depth 5 m. Length 45 cm.

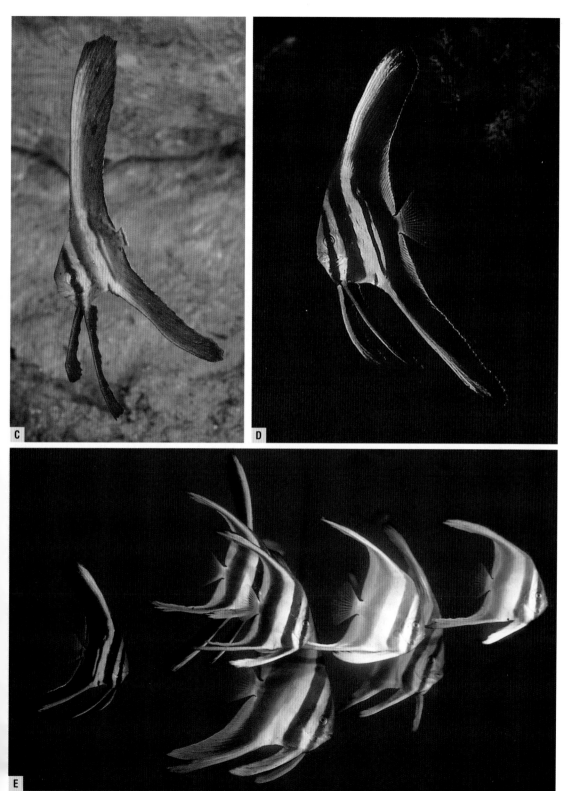

P. teira. Flores, Indonesia. Juvenile stages. **C** lonely 15 mm long juvenile in large reef pool. **D** & **E** pelagic, about 8–10 cm long.

189

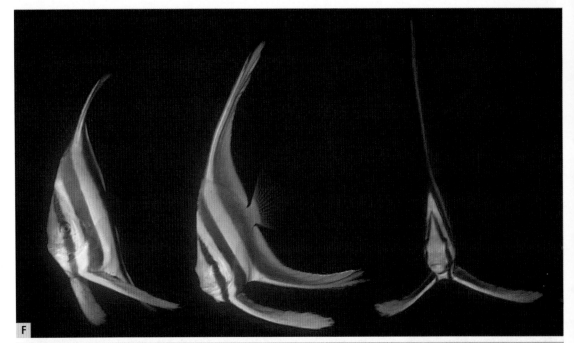

P. teira. Flores, Indonesia. Juvenile stages. **F** pelagic below *Sargassum* raft. **G** settled on reef, about 10–12 cm long.

P. teira. Bali, Indonesia. Schooling adults in open water adjacent to reef. Length about 40–45 cm. Takamasa Tonozuka.

P. teira. Flores, Indonesia. Large juveniles, about 12 cm long, settled on reef. Alison Kuiter.

Boer's Batfish
Platax boersii

Platax boersii. Bleeker, 1852.
Macassar, southern Sulawesi, Indonesia.

Widespread West Pacific from southern Japan to Indonesia and New Guinea. Possibly more widespread, but confusion with *Platax teira* and *P. orbicularis* has led to many erroneous records. Reports of *P. boersii* from the Indian Ocean are based on juveniles of *P. teira*. The juvenile stage of this species is not well known and juveniles of *P. teira* are shown in many books instead. It appears that the juveniles live in deep water and are not pelagic. The juveniles included here are of moderate size and have a more triangular shape compared to *P. teira* at a similar size. The nose profile is much more rounded. Adults are usually seen along walls or on deep slopes in 30 m depth or more. They are usually only noticed when swimming in schools, but also occur singly or in pairs. Juveniles are found on deep slopes amongst tall coral formations. Length to 40 cm.

P. boersii. Flores, Indonesia. Depth 30 m. Length 30 cm.

P. boersii. Bali, Indonesia. Depth 30 m. Length 40 cm. Takamasa Tonozuka.

C

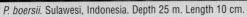

P. boersii. Sulawesi, Indonesia. Depth 25 m. Length 10 cm.

D

P. boersii. Flores, Indonesia. Length 30 cm. Depth 20 m.

E

P. boersii. Bali, Indonesia. Depth 30 m. Length 35 cm. Takamasa Tonozuka.

Round Batfish *Platax orbicularis*

Chaetodon orbicularis. Forsskål, 1775. Red Sea.

Widespread Indo-West Pacific. Adults singly or in small groups and occasionally in large schools in some areas. Occur in shallow protected coastal waters to deep, somewhat silty habitats. Often with deep shipwrecks. Juveniles identified by their shape and colour. Large juveniles are best distinguished from similar species by the dusky twin spots at the ends of the dorsal and anal fin bases. Length to 50 cm.

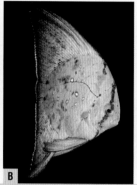
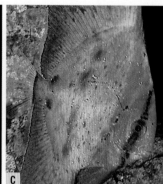

P. orbicularis. Indonesia. **A** Java. Adult, about 35 cm. **B** Sulawesi, tiny juvenile. **C** Flores, juvenile, showing diagnostic tail spots.

P. orbicularis. Red Sea. Depth 30 m. Large adult, length about 50 cm.

P. orbicularis. Indonesia. **E** Sulawesi. about 8 cm. **F** Java, about 11 cm. **C** Sulawesi, about 12 cm. All showing diagnostic tail spots.

P. orbicularis. Red Sea. Depth 30 m. Length 40–45 cm.

A

P. pinnatus. Bali, Indonesia. Depth 15 m. Length about 35 cm.

Chaetodon pinnatus. Linnaeus, 1758. East Indies.

Widespread West Pacific, ranging west to the Andaman Sea. Adults occur singly or in small groups and occasionally large schools are seen travelling over open substrates. Juveniles are often found deep along reef walls in caves with rich invertebrate growth. Adults are identified by their more protruding snout and usually have a bright yellow pectoral fin. Small juveniles are black with a bright orange outline. This gives them the appearance of a nasty tasting flatworm. Length to 35 cm.

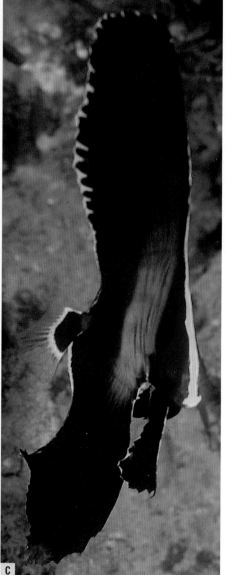

B

C

P. pinnatus. Flores, Indonesia. **B** depth 25 m. Length about 15 cm. **C** depth 30 m. Length about 10 cm.

P. pinnatus. Komodo, Indonesia. Length 20 mm. Takamasa Tonozuka.

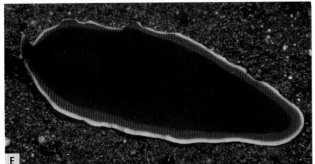
Flatworm with similar orange outline. Flores, Indonesia.

P. pinnatus. Java, Indonesia. Depth 4 m. Length 6 cm.

P. pinnatus. Queensland, Australia. Depth 25 m. Length about 35 cm.

Humped Batfish
Platax batavianus

Platax batavianus. Cuvier, 1831. Java.

West Pacific, ranging from the Malay Peninsula to eastern Australia. Adults are usually found on deep, open substrates with sparse reef or some coral heads. A solitary species, but occasionally found in pairs or small groups at depths of about 20 m or more. Small juveniles also occur in deep water and the zebra pattern serves well as camouflage when sheltering with crinoids. The striped pattern is replaced when crinoids are outgrown. Large individuals become more elongate than other batfishes and develop a hump on the forehead. The largest batfish reaching about 65 cm.

A *P. batavianus*. North-western Australia. Depth 15 m. Length about 30 cm. Jerry Allen.

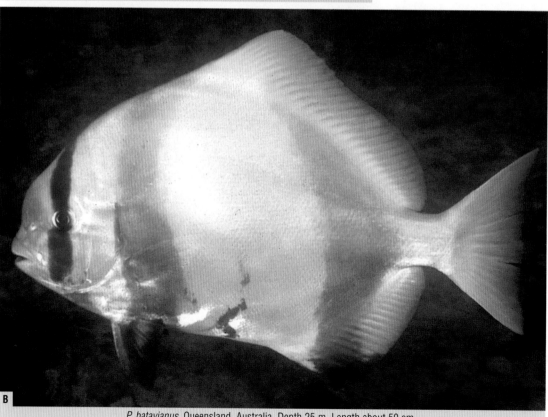

B *P. batavianus*. Queensland, Australia. Depth 25 m. Length about 50 cm.

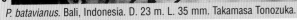

P. batavianus. Bali, Indonesia. D. 23 m. L. 35 mm. Takamasa Tonozuka.

P. batavianus. PNG. Depth 16 m. Length 40 mm.

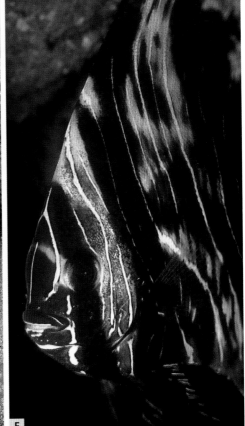

P. batavianus. Bali, Indonesia. Depth 4 m. Length about 12 cm. **E** Takamasa Tonozuka. **F** Akira Ogawa.

Masculine. Type species: *Platax novaemaculeatus* McCulloch, 1916. Monotypic. Closely related to *Platax*, but differs in meristics and shape.

Characteristics of the genus *Zabidius*.
Body almost circular in young, slightly elongate in adults, and highly compressed; mouth small, terminal, and jaws with bands of small tricuspid teeth; dorsal fin spines IX, progressively become longer and more graduated into elevated anterior soft rays; anal fin with III spines; ventral fin I, 5; caudal fin from slightly rounded in juveniles to double emarginate in adults.

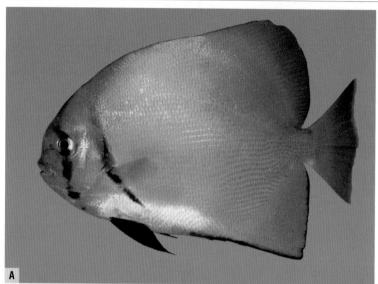

Short-fin Batfish
Zabidius novaemaculeatus

Platax novaemaculeatus.
McCulloch, 1916. Western Australia.

Only known from northern Australia and southern New Guinea. Occurs on shallow, open sand substrates adjacent to reefs, often in silty habitats. Rarely seen by divers and it is occasionally trawled. A silvery fish with 2 dark bands on its head and black ventral fins. Length to 45 cm.

Z. novaemaculeatus. **A** &. **B** north-western Australia. Adults, about 35–40 cm. Jerry Allen.

GENUS *Chaetodipterus* Lacepéde, 1802

Masculine. Type species: *Chaetodon plumierii* Bloch, 1787 (= *Chaetodon faber* Forsskål, 1782). Comprises 2 species that are divided between the Atlantic and the Pacific on the American coasts. They are commonly known as spadefishes.

Characteristics of the genus *Chaetodipterus*.
Body almost circular and highly compressed; dorsal fin deeply notched, spines IX, 3rd longest and followed by shorter spines; anal fin with II–III spines.

Atlantic Spadefish *Chaetodipterus faber*

Chaetodon faber Forsskål, 1782. Jamaica

Western Atlantic, ranging from Massachusetts to Brazil. Swims in open water, usually in small groups, but occasionally forms large schools. Adults silvery grey with dusky bands that are darker in young. They feed on the seabed as well as in mid-water on various invertebrates and also eat algae. Length to 45 cm, but reported to double that size.

A

B

C. faber. **A** Aquarium. **B** Curacao, Netherlands Antilles. Schooling adults. Depth 18 m.

Pacific Spadefish
Chaetodipterus zonatus

Ephippus zonatus Girard, 1858.
Off San Diego, California.

Eastern Pacific, ranging from southern California to Peru. A coastal species, found in sheltered bays and to a depth of about 45 m. Usually swims well above the seabed in small schools. Adults silvery with dusky bands, with juveniles browner, but bands still evident. Bands most distinct in medium sized specimens. Dark bands may fade in large individuals or when swimming above white sand and rubble substrates.
Length to 65 cm.

C. zonatus. Eastern Pacific. Length 35 cm. Jerry Allen.

GENUS *Parapsettus* Steindachner, 1875

Masculine. Type species: *Parapsettus panamensis* Steindachner, 1875. Monotypic. Similar to *Platax*, but differs in meristics and shape.

P. panamensis. Eastern Pacific. Length 25 cm. Jerry Allen.

Characteristics of the genus *Parapsettus*. Body almost circular and highly compressed; snout very short and mouth small, terminal; dorsal fin spines IX, but composed of short, free spines, mostly hidden by scales; anal fin with III spines; ventral fin I, 5 and small.

Panama Spadefish
Parapsettus panamensis

Parapsettus panamensis Steindachner, 1875. Panama.

Eastern Pacific, ranging from Gulf of California to Peru. Occurs in sand and muddy substrates in coastal bays and deep off-shore. A dull species: silvery grey with dusky to blackish fins. Identified by its short snout and small ventral fins.
Length to 40 cm.

GENUS *Ephippus* Cuvier, 1816

Masculine. Type species: *Chaetodon orbis* Bloch, 1787. Monotypic. Similar to *Chaetodipterus*, but differs in meristics and shape.

Characteristics of the genus *Ephippus*.
Body almost circular and highly compressed; snout very short and mouth small, terminal; dorsal fin deeply notched, spines IX–X, but first spine only visible in young and 4th spine longest; anal fin with III spines; ventral fin I, 5.

Orbfish *Ephippus orbis*

Chaetodon orbis Bloch, 1787.

Widespread along mainland Asia, ranging from China Seas to the Arabian Seas. Occurs in muddy bays and in deep water. Rarely seen by divers and usually taken by trawling. A small silvery species, reaching only about 20 cm.

E. orbis. After Bleeker.

GENUS *Tripterodon* Playfair, 1866

Masculine. Type species: *Tripterodon orbis* Playfair, 1866. Monotypic. Differs from *Chaetodipterus* in meristics and shape.

Characteristics of the genus *Ephippus*.
Body almost circular and highly compressed; snout very short and mouth small, terminal; dorsal fin deeply notched, spines IX–X, but first spine only visible in young; anal fin with III spines; ventral fin I, 5; caudal fin from slightly rounded in juveniles to double emarginate in adults.

African Spadefish *Tripterodon orbis*

Tripterodon orbis Playfair, 1866. Zanzibar.

Indian Ocean, from African coast to India and Sri Lanka. A schooling species, usually found close to shallow, usually silty reefs. Feeds on a great variety of benthic invertebrates as well as zooplankton. Large adults mainly silver with a touch of yellow on the spinous dorsal fin. Young and medium sized fish distinctly banded. Length to 50 cm.

A

T. orbis. Sri Lanka. Depth 15 m. Length 25 cm.

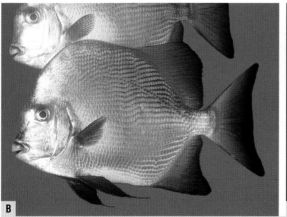

B

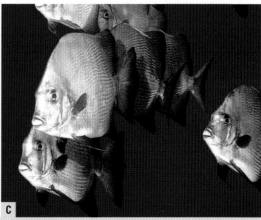

C

T. orbis. Sodwana Bay, South Africa. Depth 7 m. Length 40–45 cm. Kendall Clements.

Feminine. Type species: *Chaetodon punctatus* Linnaeus, 1758. Comprises 2 Indo-Pacific species. Commonly known as sicklefishes because of their long pectoral fins. Sometimes placed in own family Drepanidae.

Characteristics of the genus *Drepane*.
Body very deep, height about equal to standard length and highly compressed; snout profile steep; mouth low, small, and downwardly protrusible; dorsal fin spines IX–X, including small procumbent spine, mostly hidden by scales; anal fin with III spines; pectoral fin long and pointed, sickle-shaped; ventral fin I, 5.

Spotted Sicklefish *Drepane punctata*

Chaetodon punctatus Linnaeus, 1758. Asia.

Widespread Indo-West Pacific. Lives at moderate depths on open, usually muddy substrates and is mainly known from trawls, but also enters shallow estuaries. Feeds on the substrate on various invertebrates. Identified by its shape and the vertical series of small dark spots on its sides. Length to about 45 cm.

D. punctata. Ambon, Indonesia. Length 24 cm. Jerry Allen.

Banded Sicklefish *Drepane longimana*

Chaetodon longimanus Bloch & Schneider, 1801. India.

Widespread Indo-West Pacific. Occurs in shallow muddy bays and harbours as well as deeper offshore. Adults form large schools and are occasionally encountered near reefs by divers. They feed on the substrate on benthic invertebrates. Adults are bright silver and have a faint pattern of dusky bands that are more pronounced in smaller individuals or medium sized ones. length to 45 cm.

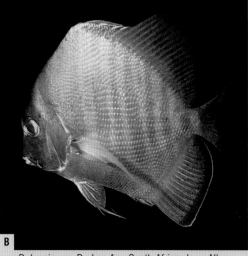

D. longimana. **A** &. **B** Oman. Phil Woodhead.

D. longimana. Durban Aq., South Africa. Jerry Allen.

FAMILY **SCATOPHAGIDAE – SCATS**

A small Indo-Pacific family with 2 genera and 2 or 3 species. They are essentially marine but prefer brackish water and penetrate freshwater far from the sea. The dorsal fin is distinctly notched and has strong spines that are preceded by a procumbent spine. The anal fin has 4 spines. The dorsal and anal fin spines are thought to be venomous and may inflict painful wounds. The two genera are separated by differences in the skin-fold under the head and scalation. Two species are included, representing one type from each genus. *Scatophagus* has small but distinct scales and *Selenotoca* has minute, almost invisible scales.

Spotted Scat *Scatophagus argus*

Chaetodon argus Linnaeus, 1766. India.

Widespread Indo-West Pacific. Occurs in harbours, estuaries and lower reaches of rivers. Tiny juveniles float with debris on the surface. These, usually less than 10 mm long, are black with orange markings. The become banded when settling on substrate and the dark bands break up into spots. Adults highly variable in their spotted patterns. Length to 35 cm.

This species is easily kept in both marine and freshwater aquariums.

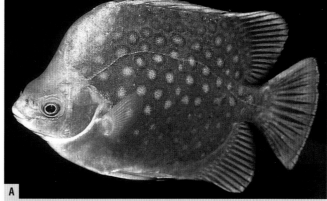

A

S. argus. Queensland, Australia. Aquarium. L. 24 cm.

B

S. argus. Hong Kong aquarium. L. 45 mm.

C

S. argus. Sri Lanka. Length 30 cm.

D

S. argus. Flores, Indonesia. D. 1 m. L. 55 mm.

E

S. argus. Java, Indonesia. Depth 1 m. Length 15 cm.

Striped Scat
Selenotoca multifasciata

Scatophagus multifasciatus Richardson, 1846.
King Georges Sound, Western Australia.

Widespread Indo-West Pacific. Occurs in small groups or schools in harbours, estuaries and lower reaches of rivers. Juveniles often in rock pools. Small juveniles banded, pattern changing with growth to bars along upper sides and spots on lower sides. Lower spots in adults may form longitudinal bands. Also called false scat or butterfish. Length to 40 cm.

This species is easily kept in both marine and freshwater aquariums.

A *S. multifasciata*. Sydney fishmarket, Australia. Adult, length 35 cm.

B C *S. multifasciata*. Qld, Australia. Aquarium. Juveniles. **B** about 50 mm. **C** about 25 mm.

D *S. multifasciata*. Pulau Putri, off Java, Indonesia. Largest about 25 cm.